BELOVED

This is YOUR year to create.
Make it an AMAZING year,
using your intuition and your
Tarot cards as a guide.

ACKNOWLEDGEMENTS

I am so proud to share the 2023 Biddy Tarot Planner with you! Of course, it would not have been possible without the help of some very special humans.

My deepest gratitude to Tássia Assis for designing the layout of the Biddy Tarot Planner; Anthony Esselmont for designing the front and back covers; Melinda Hershey for her amazing editing skills; Team Biddy for bringing the Planner to fruition; and the whole Biddy Tarot community for your ongoing love and support. Together, we have created something amazing, and I truly hope you love it!

The Tarot deck featured in the 2023 Biddy Tarot Planner is our very own Biddy Tarot Deck! Learn more at: www.biddytarot.com/deck.

Note: The exact date of lunations may vary depending on your region. This planner was made using US Pacific time. To know the exact dates for your region, go to www.timeanddate.com/moon/phases.

WELCOME

Welcome to 2023: The Year of Taking Bold Action.

This is the year to connect with your purpose, clarify your mission, and take bold action to achieve your goals. Nothing will stand in your way! And the best news is that bringing your vision to life this year will be even more possible now that you've said "yes" to your intuition and partnered with this Planner.

With the Biddy Tarot Planner by your side, you'll tune in to your Higher Self, manifest your goals and dreams, and create a life that is in full alignment with your soul's purpose — all while using Tarot as your guide.

The Biddy Tarot Planner will empower you to:

- Tap into the collective energy of each month with the intuitive Tarot forecast

- Use monthly rituals to deepen your connection with the collective energy

- Explore the blessings of each New and Full Moon

- Create personalized daily forecasts to maximize the potential of each day

- Complete seasonal Tarot spreads and connect with what each stage of the upcoming year has in store for you

This Planner has been designed to help you create an amazing year ahead, learn to trust your intuition, and allow the Tarot cards to guide you to your most deeply fulfilling year yet.

So, get out your favorite Tarot deck, grab your crystals, uncap your best markers, and prepare to get up close and personal with your divine power.

Lots of love and success,

P.S.

We love celebrating our community — and that means you! Don't forget to share LOTS of photos and videos of your Planner on Instagram, using the hashtag **#biddytarotplanner**.

Make sure you're following **@biddytarot**, as we'll be sharing even more tips to help you use Tarot to create your Year of Taking Bold Action.

FREE BONUS [VALUE $197]
BIDDY TAROT PLANNER TOOLKIT

To help you achieve your highest potential and get the most out of your 2023 Biddy Tarot Planner, I've created a free bonus Toolkit, including:

6 incredible video tutorials to set you up for success by showing you how to make the most of your planner, diving in-depth into the 2023 Card Of The Year, the New Year's Ritual, Seasonal Spreads, Lunar Spreads, and more!

2 powerful meditations to help you harness the lunar universal energy regularly, including one for the New Moon and one for the Full Moon.

A guide to navigating Mercury Retrograde and a special Mercury Retrograde Tarot spread to keep you balanced and prepared for anything.

Print-your-own Tarot cards to use inside of the Planner.

4 deep-dive Tarot spreads for self-discovery, spiritual advancement, and trusting your intuition.

Detailed guidance on how to use the Daily Tarot Card practice.

And so much more!

DOWNLOAD THE FREE PLANNER TOOLKIT AT
WWW.BIDDYTAROT.COM/2023-PLANNER-BONUS

TABLE OF CONTENTS

HOW TO MAKE THE MOST OUT OF YOUR PLANNER

To get started, here's what you will need:

- ⊙ Your favorite Tarot deck

- ⊙ Your favorite markers, pens, and pencils

- ⊙ Your free Bonus Planner Toolkit (download it at www.biddytarot.com/2023-planner-bonus)

> If you're on Instagram, use the hashtag #biddytarotplanner to post photos and videos of your Planner and Tarot spreads, and we'll share them with the Biddy Tarot community!

Here's how to create your Year of Taking Bold Action with the Biddy Tarot Planner:

FIRST, WATCH THE VIDEO TUTORIALS

I've created a series of tutorial videos to show you how to make the most of the Biddy Tarot Planner. I'll be there with you every step of the way!

For free access, go to www.biddytarot.com/2023-planner-bonus.

AT THE START OF THE YEAR...

Complete the New Year's Ritual (on page 16) — a divine experience of self-reflection, intuitive journaling, and Tarot card consultation.

And connect with the energy of the 2023 Tarot card — the Chariot. Take some time to meditate on what its energy means for you as you step into the new year.

FOR EACH SEASON...

Explore the energy of each new season with a Seasonal Tarot Spread and use that energy to set your goals and intentions for the upcoming three months.

A note on location: The seasons in this Planner have been designed for those in the Northern Hemisphere. If you are in the Southern Hemisphere, please swap the seasons so you're doing the Summer Tarot Spread in December, and so on.

AT THE START OF THE MONTH...

Reflect on the insights I've shared for each monthly Tarot card. Then take it to the next level by connecting with what that card means for you. Ask how you can harness this energy and use it throughout the month ahead.

Next, do the **ritual** associated with the Tarot card. You may do the ritual just once during the month or more frequently. You can also continue to use the ritual again in the following months if you feel called to do so.

Each month you will also find a recommended **crystal** to help you connect more deeply with that month's Tarot card. You could carry the crystal with you throughout the month, wear it, place it on your desk or in your bedroom, or even bring it out each time you do a Tarot reading — be creative!

Keep an eye out for **Mercury Retrograde**, which occurs four times this year. Renowned for wreaking havoc with communication, timing, travel, and technology, it's a good idea to avoid activities such as signing contracts, launching products, and making technical upgrades during this Retrograde.

But it's not all bad! During Mercury Retrograde, it's also the perfect time for most "re" activities: reflection, reassessment, revisiting the past, reworking or closing out a project, and re-evaluating your priorities.

For each Mercury Retrograde of the year, you can complete the Mercury Retrograde Tarot Spread (inside the Tarot Reader's Guide to Surviving Mercury Retrograde, in your Toolkit) to gain clarity through this potentially confusing time. Grab it here: www.biddytarot.com/2023-planner-bonus.

FOR EACH DAY...

At the beginning of every day, draw a Tarot card and set your intention for the day ahead. Note your card and thoughts in the Planner. At the end of the day, reflect on what you have learned and discovered based on the energy of your daily card.

For more ideas on how to do the daily Tarot card draw, check out www.biddytarot.com/daily-tarot-card.

ON THE NEW MOON AND THE FULL MOON...

Without question, the cycles of the Moon have an impact on our own personal cycles. For each New and Full Moon, do the spread that corresponds to the astrological sign of the Moon.

Reminder: On the **New Moon**, set your intentions for the next two weeks and get ready to start new projects and make way for new beginnings. On the **Full Moon**, give thanks for what you have achieved and manifested over the past two weeks, and let go of what is no longer serving you. Don't forget to clear and cleanse your energy and your space during this time.

I've created a special New Moon and Full Moon Ritual *plus* two guided visualizations so you can fully tap into the power of the lunar cycles. Access them in the Toolkit here: www.biddytarot.com/2023-planner-bonus.

A note on timing: All times and dates of the lunar cycles are in US Pacific time.

IF YOU NEED A LITTLE HELP WITH THE TAROT CARD MEANINGS...

To make the most out of the Biddy Tarot Planner, all you need is a basic knowledge of the Tarot cards — your intuition will take care of the rest! However, I know you may also want a little extra guidance along the way — so I have two helpful resources for you:

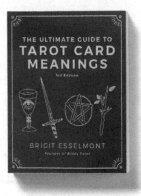

[BOOK] THE ULTIMATE GUIDE TO TAROT CARD MEANINGS

In this modern guide to the Tarot card meanings, you'll discover how to interpret the cards in your Tarot readings with ease. An Amazon best-seller, *The Ultimate Guide to Tarot Card Meanings* includes:

⊙ Detailed descriptions of the 78 Tarot cards, including upright and reversed meanings

⊙ What each card means in relationship, work, finance, spiritual, and well-being readings.

This is a must-have reference guide for all Tarot readers, from beginners to professionals, to help you quickly and easily decipher the meaning of your Tarot readings. Buy the book at www.biddytarot.com/guide.

MASTER THE TAROT
CARD MEANINGS

[ONLINE COURSE] MASTER THE TAROT CARD MEANINGS

My program, Master the Tarot Card Meanings, is the #1 online Tarot training course to help you instantly and intuitively interpret the 78 cards in the Tarot deck — without memorization.

In Master the Tarot Card Meanings, I'll show you how to build a unique personal connection with the Tarot, using simple yet powerful techniques for interpreting the cards. Plus, you'll learn the 'must know' systems within the Tarot to make learning the card meanings super simple.

Together, we'll walk through all 78 Tarot cards, so you can master each and every one of them once and for all!

Learn more at www.biddytarot.com/mtcm or start with our free training at www.biddytarot.com/webinar-mtcm.

And Lastly, Remember...

⊙ To make the most out of this Planner, check out my free video tutorials and bonuses at www.biddytarot.com/2023-planner-bonus.

⊙ Post photos of your Planner and Tarot spreads to Instagram with the hashtag #biddytarotplanner to get a shout-out!

Want to get started early?

⊙ Download the Planner pages for October, November, and December 2022 (for free!) at www.biddytarot.com/2023-planner-bonus so that you can get started right now!

2022 REFLECTION

As we come to the end of 2022, take some time to reflect on the past 12 months and prepare yourself for the year to come.

For each question, journal your intuitive thoughts first, then if you feel called to do so, draw a Tarot card to help you go deeper.

1. What were my biggest achievements for 2022?

2. What were my biggest challenges for 2022?

3. How have I developed as a person?

4. What did I learn in 2022?

5. How would I describe 2022 in just three words?

6. What aspects of 2022 can I leave behind?

7. What aspects of 2022 can I bring with me into 2023?

8. What seeds of opportunity are being planted?

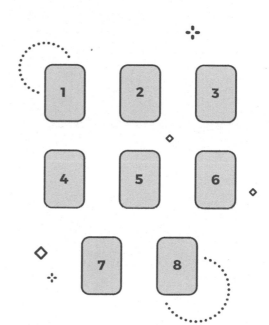

1. WHAT WERE MY BIGGEST ACHIEVEMENTS FOR 2022?

2. WHAT WERE MY BIGGEST CHALLENGES FOR 2022?

3. HOW HAVE I DEVELOPED AS A PERSON?

4. WHAT DID I LEARN IN 2022?

5. HOW WOULD I DESCRIBE 2022 IN JUST THREE WORDS?

6. WHAT ASPECTS OF 2022 CAN I LEAVE BEHIND?

7. WHAT ASPECTS OF 2022 CAN I BRING WITH ME INTO 2023?

8. WHAT SEEDS OF OPPORTUNITY ARE BEING PLANTED?

2023

2023

THE YEAR OF **THE CHARIOT** AND TAKING BOLD ACTION

2023 is the year of the Chariot (2 + 0 + 2 + 3 = 7, the Chariot) and the year of Taking Bold Action. At its core, this card — and this year — is about aligning with your purpose, setting your direction, and taking decisive action to achieve your goals. Even when obstacles or challenges stand in the way, you draw upon your focused determination, strength and willpower to push forward and get it done.

The forward momentum of the Chariot in 2023 is all possible thanks to the clarity you received in 2022 — the Year of the Lovers. Over these last 12 months, you discovered what is most important to you — your values, your purpose and your mission in life — and how to hold these close to you as you navigate the multitude of choices and opportunities available to you.

Now, as you step into 2023 — the Year of the Chariot — you are ready to take bold action in the pursuit of your purpose. Nothing will stand in your way, you are determined in your vision and you will overcome all obstacles to achieve what you truly desire. You have set your objectives and are now channeling your inner power with a fierce dedication to bring them to fruition. When you apply discipline, commitment and willpower to achieve your goals, you will succeed.

2023 is **not** the time to be passive in the hope that things will work out in your favor or that you will naturally attract what you want, without lifting a finger. No, my friend! This year is the time to take focused action and stick to the course, no matter what challenges may come your way — because, believe me, there will be challenges. You may be pulled in opposite directions and find your strength and conviction tested. Others may try to block you, distract you, or drag down the pursuit of your goal. But the Chariot is an invitation to draw upon your willpower and home in on what's essential to you, so you can push past the obstacles in your way.

The Chariot encourages you to assert yourself and be courageous. Be bold in expressing your desires and laying down your boundaries; otherwise, you will not get your way. You need to have faith in yourself and know fundamentally who you are and what you stand for (thus building off the personal belief systems and values established through the Lovers card).

If you are curious about whether you have what it takes to achieve your mission or complete an important project this year, the Chariot is a sign of success, so long as you keep your focus and remain confident in your abilities. You need to use your willpower and self-discipline to concentrate on the task at hand. You can't cut corners or take the easy route, or you will fail. Instead, see this endeavor as a test of your strength and conviction, and recognize that victory is within reach, but it's up to you to follow through.

As with all cards in the Tarot deck, there is a shadow side to the Chariot. There may be times when you are pushing too hard on a project or a goal. In an attempt to overcome all obstacles and try harder to make it work, you only experience more and more resistance. It is as if the odds are stacked against you. Pay attention to this subtle but important shift as this may be a sign from the Universe that you are 'off-track' and instead of 'trying harder', you need to change course. Find the balance between taking action and being in flow.

Overall, 2023 is a powerful year for making progress, overcoming obstacles and achieving your goals. Maximize this opportunity through setting a clear direction with milestones along the way, taking bold action, and celebrating your achievements throughout the next 12 months.

RITUAL: ACTIVATING YOUR MISSION

Find a quiet place where you won't be disturbed. Take out the Chariot card and reflect on its energy. Notice the imagery, colors, and symbols that stand out to you today. Then, when you're ready, light a candle, and burn some rosemary or frankincense oil.

Reflect on what you want to achieve this year. What are the big goals or milestones that would make a massive impact in your life and others'? Write these down in your notebook.

Then, reflect on all the possible challenges that might stand in the way of you achieving your goals. How will you overcome these challenges?

And finally, what are the steps you need to take to set yourself up for success this year? Write these down.

Now, to activate your mission, close your eyes and take in a few deep breaths as you feel your body relax. Bring your energy and attention into your Higher Mind. Then imagine as if you have successfully accomplished all of your goals this year. Bring this up in your mind's eye, with all the sights, sounds, smells and feelings, as if it were real. Feel the feeling of success and achievement. When you're ready, gradually bring your attention back into the room and open your eyes. Blow out the candle, as you say aloud, "And so it is".

JOURNALING PROMPTS

Use these journaling prompts throughout the year to help you stay in alignment with the Chariot's energy:

⊘ What does success mean to me?

⊘ What do I truly desire and why is it important to me?

⊘ How can I overcome my challenges and move forward with my desires?

⊘ When is it OK to quit or change direction?

⊘ What does it mean to stay in control?

ⓧ REFLECT BACK ON 2014 — THE PREVIOUS YEAR OF THE CHARIOT

⊘ What have I achieved in the last 9 years?

⊘ How has my life's mission changed and evolved? What has stayed the same?

⊘ What have I discovered about myself as I have actively pursued my goals?

INSIGHTS

NEW YEAR'S RITUAL

This New Year's Ritual is a beautiful, empowering way to start the new year! You'll be connecting with your Higher Self and envisioning what you truly want to manifest in the year to come. This is about positive change and transformation at a deep, symbolic level that will help you to create an abundant, super-charged year ahead.

I encourage you to use this ritual as a guide only. Rituals become even more powerful when **you** create them, so use this as a starting point and then get creative with what you want to include.

Ready? Let's do it!

STEP 1: CREATE YOUR SACRED SPACE

Gather everything you need for the ritual and begin to create your sacred space.

Next, set up your altar. Your altar doesn't have to be super fancy. Simply use items that represent what you want to manifest in 2023. You can include crystals, Tarot cards, jewelry, flowers, rocks — whatever helps you to create a sacred intention for your ritual.

Place the candles in and around your altar. When you're all set up and ready, switch off the lights, and light the candles.

Take a moment to ground yourself. Close your eyes and take in a few deep breaths. Connect in with the Earth energy and the Universal energy, feeling yourself filled with a beautiful white light.

STEP 2: REFLECT ON THE PAST YEAR

Reflect on the year that was 2022. What did you experience? What were the highs? What were the lows? And what did you learn along the way?

To support you in this process, use the New Year's Tarot Spread on page 20. Draw the first 2 cards and write your insights in the spaces provided on pages 20 and 21.

Then, write your thoughts about the past year on the next page.

BEFORE YOU START, YOU WILL NEED...

- ⊙ Your Biddy Tarot Planner

- ⊙ Your favorite Tarot deck — the Biddy Tarot Deck is a great place to start (available via www.biddytarot.com/deck)

- ⊙ Your favorite markers

- ⊙ At least one candle and some matches

- ⊙ An herbal bundle for clearing and cleansing

- ⊙ Items for your altar. These are symbols of what you want to create in 2023, such as an image of your ideal relationship, a flower for beauty, a seed pod for starting something new — you choose!

- ⊙ At least one hour of uninterrupted time — lock the door, turn off your phone, do whatever you need to protect your sacred space

- ⊙ (Optional) Your favorite crystals — I recommend citrine for abundance and clear quartz for clarity

- ⊙ The New Year's Tarot Spread (page 20)

Remember, if you would like extra guidance for the New Year's Ritual, watch the free video tutorials at www.biddytarot.com/2023-planner-bonus

INSIGHTS

Take the herbal bundle and light it. Then, wave the smoke around your body, front and back, as you cleanse your aura and release any old energy that may be clinging to you. For each item on your list, say aloud, "I release myself of... {insert what you want to release}."

When you feel complete, say aloud three times, **"I give thanks for the past year. I release what no longer serves me. And I welcome new opportunities with open arms."**

STEP 3: VISUALIZE WHAT YOU WANT TO CREATE IN 2023

Now, close your eyes and start to imagine what you want to create in 2023.

Think about what you want to create in your relationships. Imagine it as if it were a movie in your mind, experiencing everything you want to experience in your relationships for 2023. See yourself being an active participant in the movie. See what you see. Hear what you hear. Feel what you feel. Taste what you taste. And smell what you smell. Create a full sensory experience.

When you're ready, wipe the movie screen clean, and bring up a new movie, this time about your career, work and finances. What do you want to create in your material world? Create a full sensory experience.

When you're complete, bring up the next movie for your health and well-being. And after that, your personal development. What do you want to create?

When you feel complete, open your eyes, and write down your experiences on the next page.

Next, take out your Tarot cards and continue with Cards 3 to 9 of the New Year's Tarot Spread. Write your cards and insights in the space provided on pages 21 to 23.

RELATIONSHIPS

HEALTH AND WELL-BEING

CAREER AND FINANCES

PERSONAL DEVELOPMENT

STEP 4: MANIFEST YOUR GOALS FOR 2023

Read over your insights from Step 3 and choose 10 things you want to manifest in 2023 (e.g. I want to be fit and healthy, or I want to take a 3-month vacation).

Then, change these to "I am" statements (yes, even if they sound a little funny). For example, "I AM fit and healthy" or "I AM enjoying a 3-month vacation." Take a moment to feel the energy and the vibration of these "I am" statements — super powerful, right?!

Now, complete your New Year Tarot Spread from Cards 10 to 12 and write your cards and insights in the spaces provided on pages 23 and 24.

Finally, close your eyes and visualize the energy of what you want to create as a bright white light. Imagine it as a ball of light radiating within your solar plexus (just above your belly button). Then imagine the ball of light getting bigger and bigger, filling your body, flowing through your aura, and illuminating out into the world. This is your power, your determination, your ability to manifest your goals, just as you see them. And so it is done. When you are ready, gently open your eyes.

STEP 5: CLOSE THE SPACE

Before you close the space, check in with your Higher Self and ask if there is anything else that needs to be done before this ritual is complete. Sometimes your intuition may guide you towards another sacred activity before you know for sure that you are done.

When you're ready, say a prayer of thanks to your Higher Self for guiding you along this process. Then, say out loud, "And so it is."

Blow out the candles, turn on the lights, then pack up the space. You may wish to leave part of your altar there or move it somewhere more convenient, so you have a visual reminder of this beautiful ritual that you have gifted yourself.

INSIGHTS

NEW YEAR'S TAROT SPREAD

Gain the clarity you need for your Year of Spiritual Awakening with the New Year's Tarot Spread. This is a powerful spread to use at the start of the year. Or, even on your birthday, to gain valuable insight into what you might experience during your next year of life.

1. The previous year in summary

2. Lessons learned from the past year

3. Aspirations for the next 12 months

4. What empowers you in reaching your aspirations

5. What may stand in the way of reaching your aspirations

6. Your relationships and emotions in the coming year

7. Your career, work, and finances

8. Your health and well-being

9. Your spiritual energy and inner fulfillment

10. What you most need to focus on in the year ahead

11. Your most important lesson for the coming year

12. Overall, where you are headed in the next 12 months

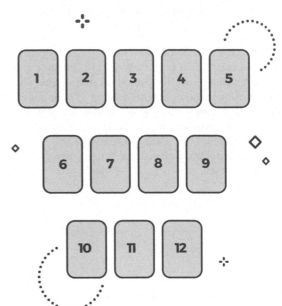

1. THE PREVIOUS YEAR IN SUMMARY

Excited with what 2023 might bring you? Post a pic of your spread using the hashtag
#biddytarotplanner and we'll share with the Biddy Tarot community!

2. LESSONS LEARNED FROM THE PAST YEAR

3. ASPIRATIONS FOR THE NEXT 12 MONTHS

4. WHAT EMPOWERS YOU IN REACHING YOUR ASPIRATIONS

5. WHAT MAY STAND IN THE WAY OF REACHING YOUR ASPIRATIONS

6. YOUR RELATIONSHIPS AND EMOTIONS IN THE COMING YEAR

7. YOUR CAREER, WORK, AND FINANCES

8. YOUR HEALTH AND WELL-BEING

9. YOUR SPIRITUAL ENERGY AND INNER FULFILLMENT

10. WHAT YOU MOST NEED TO FOCUS ON IN THE YEAR AHEAD

11. YOUR MOST IMPORTANT LESSON FOR THE COMING YEAR

12. OVERALL, WHERE YOU ARE HEADED IN THE NEXT 12 MONTHS

JANUARY

CHARIOT

VII

THE CHARIOT

What better way to start off a new year than with the action-oriented Chariot? The Chariot inspires you to make aligned decisions with a fresh burst of willpower, determination, and strength. January is a potent time to harness the energy of this powerful card. Here's how to harness this Chariot energy to set goals for the year ahead:

⊙ **Start by clarifying your goals for the year.** Write them down, as well as any challenges you might anticipate along the way.

⊙ **Set your direction.** What actions will you need to take to make your goals a reality?

⊙ **Write down a statement of your intention.** For each goal, write down: "I will achieve (GOAL) by (DATE) by doing (ACTION)." This helps set your goals in stone so you can embark on a year of bold action.

If you ever feel pulled in multiple directions or distracted by different opportunities, bring your attention back to the goals on your list and choose the path that's most in alignment with your higher purpose. When you feel like you've strayed from your path, draw on your willpower, strength and inner voice to stay focused.

☙ RITUAL: DAILY INTENTIONS

To activate your Chariot energy this month, try out this Chariot-inspired morning ritual.

⊙ Place the Chariot card in front of you and draw in its energy of pure focus and determination.

⊙ Then, contemplate your day. What 3 things do you want to accomplish today that will get you closer to your goals? Write these down in your journal.

⊙ Next, consider what might stand in the way of you being able to complete these 3 things. How might you overcome these potential challenges? Write them down.

⊙ To close the ritual, remind yourself of your 3 actions for today, knowing that you have what you need to overcome any challenges. Then, start taking action, fueled by the strength of your commitment and dedication to do what it takes to achieve your goals.

☙ CRYSTAL: CHALCEDONY

Chalcedony helps to maintain balance and harmony in your life while soothing and eliminating fears and anxieties. It clears the way for you to manifest your goals and bring your ideas to action. Keep one on your desk to ground and protect you from negative influences and to inspire optimism for the future.

INSIGHTS

JANUARY 6

FULL MOON IN CANCER

The Full Moon in Cancer is *the* best time to release any feelings that you're holding onto. Dive into your emotional world and set empowering intentions around what feelings you want to release.

1. What new feelings are coming up for me right now that need to be released?

2. Where do I need to empower myself to be more vulnerable in my relationships?

3. How might I benefit from setting boundaries?

4. How can I level-up my self-care practice?

5. What do I need to know about creating sacred space in my home?

6. What new approach can I take to support my emotional well-being?

INSIGHTS

JANUARY 21

NEW MOON IN

An Aquarius New Moon is an opportunity to set out-of-the-box intentions. Let go of what others think or expect and make your plans according to what you *really* want.

1. What unique gifts do I bring to the table?

2. How can I best utilize these gifts for the betterment of humanity?

3. Where would I most like to see social change and equality?

4. How am I best placed to communicate my ideas with the world?

5. How can I connect with others who align with my vision for the future?

6. Which areas of my life would benefit from expressing vulnerability?

INSIGHTS

JAN 01 SUNDAY   CARD OF THE DAY:

▷ INTENTION   ▷ REFLECTION

JAN 02 MONDAY   CARD OF THE DAY:

▷ INTENTION   ▷ REFLECTION

JAN 03 TUESDAY   CARD OF THE DAY:

▷ INTENTION   ▷ REFLECTION

JAN 04 WEDNESDAY   CARD OF THE DAY:

▷ INTENTION   ▷ REFLECTION

JAN 05 THURSDAY   CARD OF THE DAY:

▷ INTENTION   ▷ REFLECTION

JAN 06 FRIDAY | ● *Full Moon in Cancer*   CARD OF THE DAY:

▷ INTENTION   ▷ REFLECTION

JAN 07 SATURDAY   CARD OF THE DAY:

▷ INTENTION   ▷ REFLECTION

JAN 08 SUNDAY

CARD OF THE DAY:

▷ INTENTION

▷ REFLECTION

JAN 09 MONDAY

CARD OF THE DAY:

▷ INTENTION

▷ REFLECTION

JAN 10 TUESDAY

CARD OF THE DAY:

▷ INTENTION

▷ REFLECTION

JAN 11 WEDNESDAY

CARD OF THE DAY:

▷ INTENTION

▷ REFLECTION

JAN 12 THURSDAY

CARD OF THE DAY:

▷ INTENTION

▷ REFLECTION

JAN 13 FRIDAY

CARD OF THE DAY:

▷ INTENTION

▷ REFLECTION

JAN 14 SATURDAY

CARD OF THE DAY:

▷ INTENTION

▷ REFLECTION

JAN 15   SUNDAY   CARD OF THE DAY:

▷ INTENTION   ▷ REFLECTION

JAN 16   MONDAY   CARD OF THE DAY:

▷ INTENTION   ▷ REFLECTION

JAN 17   TUESDAY   CARD OF THE DAY:

▷ INTENTION   ▷ REFLECTION

JAN 18   WEDNESDAY | *Mercury Retrograde ends*   CARD OF THE DAY:

▷ INTENTION   ▷ REFLECTION

JAN 19   THURSDAY   CARD OF THE DAY:

▷ INTENTION   ▷ REFLECTION

JAN 20   FRIDAY   CARD OF THE DAY:

▷ INTENTION   ▷ REFLECTION

JAN 21   SATURDAY | ○ *New Moon in Aquarius*   CARD OF THE DAY:

▷ INTENTION   ▷ REFLECTION

JAN 22 SUNDAY

CARD OF THE DAY:

▷ INTENTION

▷ REFLECTION

JAN 23 MONDAY

CARD OF THE DAY:

▷ INTENTION

▷ REFLECTION

JAN 24 TUESDAY

CARD OF THE DAY:

▷ INTENTION

▷ REFLECTION

JAN 25 WEDNESDAY

CARD OF THE DAY:

▷ INTENTION

▷ REFLECTION

JAN 26 THURSDAY

CARD OF THE DAY:

▷ INTENTION

▷ REFLECTION

JAN 27 FRIDAY

CARD OF THE DAY:

▷ INTENTION

▷ REFLECTION

JAN 28 SATURDAY

CARD OF THE DAY:

▷ INTENTION

▷ REFLECTION

JAN 29   SUNDAY   CARD OF THE DAY:

▷ INTENTION   ▷ REFLECTION

JAN 30   MONDAY   CARD OF THE DAY:

▷ INTENTION   ▷ REFLECTION

JAN 31   TUESDAY   CARD OF THE DAY:

▷ INTENTION   ▷ REFLECTION

INSIGHTS

FEBRUARY

JUSTICE

This month, you (and the collective) are invited to take full responsibility for your actions. When we own up to everything that we are, we open the door for justice and fairness for everyone. The Justice card states that if you've acted within the bounds of what is right and fair, then you'll be rewarded. But if you've strayed outside these ethical boundaries, the truth will be known and you'll be called out to own up to your truth. You may also have an important decision to make in February. While the decision isn't clear-cut, it may have long-term consequences, so choose wisely! Weigh up each option and choose your path consciously by connecting with your intuition and asking for the answer that's most aligned with the highest good of all.

☸ RITUAL: KARMIC CLEANSING

We've all done things we regret, but it's always possible to heal and move forward. This ritual helps you to cleanse your karma by owning your choices, releasing your guilt and taking the next right action.

- ⊙ Begin by finding the Justice card, and take some time to connect with its energy.

- ⊙ Then, reflect on something you've done recently that you regret or that may have hurt others. On a piece of paper, write down what happened in 2-3 sentences.

- ⊙ Then, write down the choices you made along the way and why you made those choices.

- ⊙ Release this by tearing up the pieces of paper, as you say out loud, "I own the choices I made and I forgive myself, knowing I did the best I could with what I had."

- ⊙ Then, on a fresh piece of paper, write down everything you need to do to make it right. Make this your focus for the month (or even the next few months) as you cleanse your karma for good.

⚗ CRYSTAL: CLEAR QUARTZ

Known as "The Master Healer," clear quartz radiates high vibes to help you clear your mind, body, and spirit of clutter. This gorgeous stone helps you see all the blocks holding you back from forgiving yourself. Wear a quartz stone or hold one during meditation as you're working through any tough emotions.

INSIGHTS

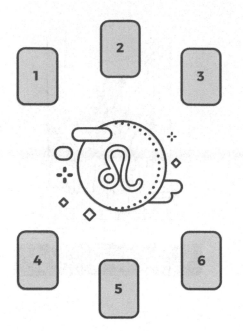

FEBRUARY 5

FULL MOON IN LEO

The Full Moon in Leo invites you to feel into the fullness of creativity and play. Celebrate your unique warmth and brilliance as you bathe in this wonderful energy.

1. What am I most proud of having achieved in the last six months?

2. How has my past courage impacted my personal growth?

3. What are some limiting beliefs I hold about myself?

4. What new stories can I tell myself instead?

5. Where in my life might I need to be more humble?

6. How could I express myself more authentically this year?

INSIGHTS

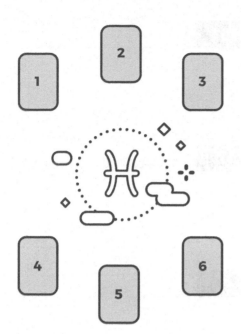

NEW MOON IN PISCES

The Pisces New Moon is the perfect time to let your imagination run wild and dream big. Tap into your intuition and set intentions to bring your visions to life.

1. How can I connect more deeply with my intuition?

2. What can I do to bring myself into alignment with the highest good?

3. What am I currently manifesting in my life?

4. How can I align my emotions to support positive manifestations?

5. What new creative projects am I called to begin now?

6. How can I further develop my spiritual practice?

INSIGHTS

FEB 01 WEDNESDAY

CARD OF THE DAY:

▷ INTENTION

▷ REFLECTION

FEB 02 THURSDAY

CARD OF THE DAY:

▷ INTENTION

▷ REFLECTION

FEB 03 FRIDAY

CARD OF THE DAY:

▷ INTENTION

▷ REFLECTION

FEB 04 SATURDAY

CARD OF THE DAY:

▷ INTENTION

▷ REFLECTION

FEB 05 SUNDAY | ● *Full Moon in Leo*

CARD OF THE DAY:

▷ INTENTION

▷ REFLECTION

FEB 06 MONDAY

CARD OF THE DAY:

▷ INTENTION

▷ REFLECTION

FEB 07 TUESDAY

CARD OF THE DAY:

▷ INTENTION

▷ REFLECTION

FEB 08   WEDNESDAY   CARD OF THE DAY:

▷ INTENTION   ▷ REFLECTION

FEB 09   THURSDAY   CARD OF THE DAY:

▷ INTENTION   ▷ REFLECTION

FEB 10   FRIDAY   CARD OF THE DAY:

▷ INTENTION   ▷ REFLECTION

FEB 11   SATURDAY   CARD OF THE DAY:

▷ INTENTION   ▷ REFLECTION

FEB 12   SUNDAY   CARD OF THE DAY:

▷ INTENTION   ▷ REFLECTION

FEB 13   MONDAY   CARD OF THE DAY:

▷ INTENTION   ▷ REFLECTION

FEB 14   TUESDAY   CARD OF THE DAY:

▷ INTENTION   ▷ REFLECTION

FEB 15 WEDNESDAY

CARD OF THE DAY:

▷ INTENTION

▷ REFLECTION

FEB 16 THURSDAY

CARD OF THE DAY:

▷ INTENTION

▷ REFLECTION

FEB 17 FRIDAY

CARD OF THE DAY:

▷ INTENTION

▷ REFLECTION

FEB 18 SATURDAY

CARD OF THE DAY:

▷ INTENTION

▷ REFLECTION

FEB 19 SUNDAY | ○ *New Moon in Pisces*

CARD OF THE DAY:

▷ INTENTION

▷ REFLECTION

FEB 20 MONDAY

CARD OF THE DAY:

▷ INTENTION

▷ REFLECTION

FEB 21 TUESDAY

CARD OF THE DAY:

▷ INTENTION

▷ REFLECTION

FEB 22　WEDNESDAY

CARD OF THE DAY:

▷ INTENTION

▷ REFLECTION

FEB 23　THURSDAY

CARD OF THE DAY:

▷ INTENTION

▷ REFLECTION

FEB 24　FRIDAY

CARD OF THE DAY:

▷ INTENTION

▷ REFLECTION

FEB 25　SATURDAY

CARD OF THE DAY:

▷ INTENTION

▷ REFLECTION

FEB 26　SUNDAY

CARD OF THE DAY:

▷ INTENTION

▷ REFLECTION

FEB 27　MONDAY

CARD OF THE DAY:

▷ INTENTION

▷ REFLECTION

FEB 28　TUESDAY

CARD OF THE DAY:

▷ INTENTION

▷ REFLECTION

MARCH

HIGH PRIESTESS

In March, the High Priestess calls you to create alignment between your inner and outer worlds. Explore your *inner world* through meditation, journaling, reading Tarot or spending time in nature. Listen deeply to the voice of your inner wisdom. What messages and advice does she have for you? Are you listening to her intuitive nudges? Then, how can you bring this inner wisdom into your *outer world*? You have the opportunity to live a multi-dimensional, highly conscious life if you can integrate your intuition into your everyday experiences. The following ritual is a powerful practice to help you translate your intuitive messages into action.

THE HIGH PRIESTESS

 ### RITUAL: DAILY TUNING IN

You'll need an amethyst and labradorite crystal for this ritual (or your favorite crystals for intuition).

- Lay down on your back and place the amethyst on your third eye chakra (between your brows) and the labradorite on your heart chakra (in the center of your chest).

- As you inhale, visualize white light flowing into an illuminating indigo ball in the center of your third eye chakra. As you exhale, visualize the light softening and growing bigger.

- Continue this visualization for a few minutes. When you feel connected, ask yourself, "What does my Highest Self want me to know right now?" Continue to breathe into your third eye chakra and invite your inner wisdom to speak to you.

- When you feel ready, sit up and write down the messages that came through for you.

CRYSTAL: LABRADORITE

Labradorite awakens you to your inner consciousness. It takes you deep within to access your Higher Self, your inner being, and your source of all wisdom. It is a powerful stone that aids in intuition, psychic abilities, clairvoyance, and a deeper connection to one's true self.

INSIGHTS

MARCH 7

FULL MOON IN VIRGO

The Virgo full moon invites you to honor the ways you are serving the world and the places you are creating order from chaos.

1. What can I offer to my family and friends to be of the highest service?

2. Which areas of my life might benefit from creating order?

3. How might I benefit from working hard in the next six months?

4. How can I limit clutter in my physical space?

5. What can I do to better support my mental clarity?

6. How can I best support healthy emotional expression?

INSIGHTS

NEW MOON
IN ARIES

Use the extra dose of Aries courage to set bold intentions at this new moon. What risks would you take if you knew you would succeed?

1. What steps should I take to bring myself into alignment with my true desires?

2. Where can I channel my passion to reap rewards in the next six months?

3. What can I become more excited about?

4. How could I be more compassionate toward others?

5. What can I do to bolster my self-confidence?

6. How can I handle conflict more effectively?

INSIGHTS

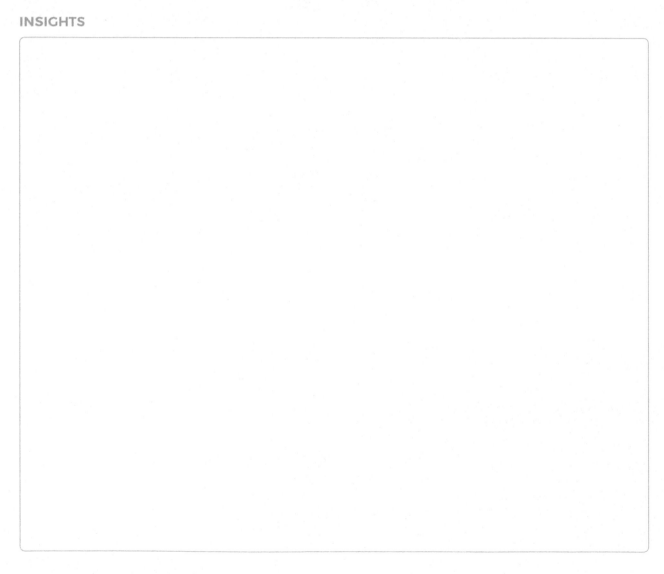

MAR 01 WEDNESDAY   CARD OF THE DAY:

▷ INTENTION   ▷ REFLECTION

MAR 02 THURSDAY   CARD OF THE DAY:

▷ INTENTION   ▷ REFLECTION

MAR 03 FRIDAY   CARD OF THE DAY:

▷ INTENTION   ▷ REFLECTION

MAR 04 SATURDAY   CARD OF THE DAY:

▷ INTENTION   ▷ REFLECTION

MAR 05 SUNDAY   CARD OF THE DAY:

▷ INTENTION   ▷ REFLECTION

MAR 06 MONDAY   CARD OF THE DAY:

▷ INTENTION   ▷ REFLECTION

MAR 07 TUESDAY | ● *Full Moon in Virgo*   CARD OF THE DAY:

▷ INTENTION   ▷ REFLECTION

MAR 08 WEDNESDAY   CARD OF THE DAY:

▷ INTENTION   ▷ REFLECTION

MAR 09 THURSDAY   CARD OF THE DAY:

▷ INTENTION   ▷ REFLECTION

MAR 10 FRIDAY   CARD OF THE DAY:

▷ INTENTION   ▷ REFLECTION

MAR 11 SATURDAY   CARD OF THE DAY:

▷ INTENTION   ▷ REFLECTION

MAR 12 SUNDAY   CARD OF THE DAY:

▷ INTENTION   ▷ REFLECTION

MAR 13 MONDAY   CARD OF THE DAY:

▷ INTENTION   ▷ REFLECTION

MAR 14 TUESDAY   CARD OF THE DAY:

▷ INTENTION   ▷ REFLECTION

MAR 15 WEDNESDAY

CARD OF THE DAY:

▷ INTENTION

▷ REFLECTION

MAR 16 THURSDAY

CARD OF THE DAY:

▷ INTENTION

▷ REFLECTION

MAR 17 FRIDAY

CARD OF THE DAY:

▷ INTENTION

▷ REFLECTION

MAR 18 SATURDAY

CARD OF THE DAY:

▷ INTENTION

▷ REFLECTION

MAR 19 SUNDAY

CARD OF THE DAY:

▷ INTENTION

▷ REFLECTION

MAR 20 MONDAY

CARD OF THE DAY:

▷ INTENTION

▷ REFLECTION

MAR 21 TUESDAY | ○ *New Moon in Aries*

CARD OF THE DAY:

▷ INTENTION

▷ REFLECTION

MAR 22 WEDNESDAY   CARD OF THE DAY:

▷ INTENTION   ▷ REFLECTION

MAR 23 THURSDAY   CARD OF THE DAY:

▷ INTENTION   ▷ REFLECTION

MAR 24 FRIDAY   CARD OF THE DAY:

▷ INTENTION   ▷ REFLECTION

MAR 25 SATURDAY   CARD OF THE DAY:

▷ INTENTION   ▷ REFLECTION

MAR 26 SUNDAY   CARD OF THE DAY:

▷ INTENTION   ▷ REFLECTION

MAR 27 MONDAY   CARD OF THE DAY:

▷ INTENTION   ▷ REFLECTION

MAR 28 TUESDAY   CARD OF THE DAY:

▷ INTENTION   ▷ REFLECTION

MAR 29 WEDNESDAY

CARD OF THE DAY:

▷ INTENTION

▷ REFLECTION

MAR 30 THURSDAY

CARD OF THE DAY:

▷ INTENTION

▷ REFLECTION

MAR 31 FRIDAY

CARD OF THE DAY:

▷ INTENTION

▷ REFLECTION

INSIGHTS

SPRING EQUINOX SPREAD

The Spring Equinox (March 20, 2:24pm PT; September 23, 4:49pm AEST) honors new growth and opportunity. The seeds have been planted and nurtured by the rain, now they are emerging from the earth into the brightness of the sunlight, blossoming into beautiful flowers, fruit, and foliage. Springtime is filled with color, scents, and a feeling of excitement and anticipation of what's to come. It's the perfect time to explore new possibilities, start new projects, and truly bloom under the rays of this positive light.

Use the following Tarot spread around the time of the Spring Equinox to connect with this sacred energy.

1. What has emerged for me over the Winter period?

2. What lessons have I learned?

3. What new seeds are beginning to sprout?

4. How can I nurture these new opportunities?

5. How am I truly blossoming?

6. How can I best embrace the Spring energy?

INSIGHTS

INSIGHTS

SPRING EQUINOX INTENTIONS

Holding the energy and insight of your Spring Equinox Tarot Reading, set your intentions for the next three months:

APRIL

XXI

THE WORLD

THE WORLD

April brings a sense of wholeness and completion as all your triumphs and tribulations come full circle. Everything you've experienced, good and bad, has led you to this moment, and you feel immensely grateful for everything you've created. You also feel a deep connection with your global community. Find ways to join together around a unified cause, through online communities, global projects, or travel. Spread your reach to those who are different from you, but with whom you still feel a connection. Learn more about different cultures and ways of life, and you may find that you share many similarities.

☸ RITUAL: GRATITUDE AND CLOSURE

- ⊚ Take out the World card from your Tarot deck and place it in front of you, drawing in its energy.

- ⊚ Light a candle and say out loud, "I open this sacred space and give thanks for all that I have experienced."

- ⊚ Now, visualize your achievements, opportunities, and challenges of the past year and write them down in your journal.

- ⊚ Then, reflect on what you've learned from the year and write these lessons down.

- ⊚ Finally, reflect on how you can bring a sense of closure and completion to this cycle.

- ⊚ To end the ritual, blow out the candle, saying out loud, "I close this sacred space and give thanks for all that I've experienced."

⚗ CRYSTAL: AMETHYST

A high-vibrational and protective stone, Amethyst balances out the highs and lows of life, bringing peace and understanding. It helps you to remain focused and appreciative of all the blessings around you.

INSIGHTS

FULL MOON IN LIBRA

The Libra Full Moon invites you to revel in beauty and release anything that negatively impacts your sense of harmony and balance.

1. What support might help me make the best choices?

2. What can I do to create more balance in my closest relationships?

3. Where is the greatest imbalance in my life right now?

4. What do I need to release in order to be more objective moving forward?

5. What do I need to do to feel more confident in my decision-making?

6. How can I manifest more beauty in my life?

INSIGHTS

NEW MOON IN ARIES

Use the extra dose of Aries courage to set bold intentions at this new moon solar eclipse. What risks would you take if you knew you would succeed?

1. What are the next steps to bring myself into alignment with my true desires?

2. Where can I channel my passion to reap rewards in the next six months?

3. What can I become more excited about?

4. How could I be more compassionate toward others?

5. What can I do to bolster my self-confidence?

6. How can I handle conflict more effectively?

INSIGHTS

APR 01 SATURDAY
CARD OF THE DAY:

▷ INTENTION

▷ REFLECTION

APR 02 SUNDAY
CARD OF THE DAY:

▷ INTENTION

▷ REFLECTION

APR 03 MONDAY
CARD OF THE DAY:

▷ INTENTION

▷ REFLECTION

APR 04 TUESDAY
CARD OF THE DAY:

▷ INTENTION

▷ REFLECTION

APR 05 WEDNESDAY | ● *Full Moon in Libra*
CARD OF THE DAY:

▷ INTENTION

▷ REFLECTION

APR 06 THURSDAY
CARD OF THE DAY:

▷ INTENTION

▷ REFLECTION

APR 07 FRIDAY
CARD OF THE DAY:

▷ INTENTION

▷ REFLECTION

APR 08 SATURDAY

CARD OF THE DAY:

▷ INTENTION

▷ REFLECTION

APR 09 SUNDAY

CARD OF THE DAY:

▷ INTENTION

▷ REFLECTION

APR 10 MONDAY

CARD OF THE DAY:

▷ INTENTION

▷ REFLECTION

APR 11 TUESDAY

CARD OF THE DAY:

▷ INTENTION

▷ REFLECTION

APR 12 WEDNESDAY

CARD OF THE DAY:

▷ INTENTION

▷ REFLECTION

APR 13 THURSDAY

CARD OF THE DAY:

▷ INTENTION

▷ REFLECTION

APR 14 FRIDAY

CARD OF THE DAY:

▷ INTENTION

▷ REFLECTION

APR 15   SATURDAY   CARD OF THE DAY:

▷ INTENTION   ▷ REFLECTION

APR 16   SUNDAY   CARD OF THE DAY:

▷ INTENTION   ▷ REFLECTION

APR 17   MONDAY   CARD OF THE DAY:

▷ INTENTION   ▷ REFLECTION

APR 18   TUESDAY   CARD OF THE DAY:

▷ INTENTION   ▷ REFLECTION

APR 19   WEDNESDAY | ☼ *New Moon in Aries*   CARD OF THE DAY:

▷ INTENTION   ▷ REFLECTION

APR 20   THURSDAY   CARD OF THE DAY:

▷ INTENTION   ▷ REFLECTION

APR 21   FRIDAY | *Mercury Retrograde begins*   CARD OF THE DAY:

▷ INTENTION   ▷ REFLECTION

APR 22 SATURDAY

CARD OF THE DAY:

▷ INTENTION

▷ REFLECTION

APR 23 SUNDAY

CARD OF THE DAY:

▷ INTENTION

▷ REFLECTION

APR 24 MONDAY

CARD OF THE DAY:

▷ INTENTION

▷ REFLECTION

APR 25 TUESDAY

CARD OF THE DAY:

▷ INTENTION

▷ REFLECTION

APR 26 WEDNESDAY

CARD OF THE DAY:

▷ INTENTION

▷ REFLECTION

APR 27 THURSDAY

CARD OF THE DAY:

▷ INTENTION

▷ REFLECTION

APR 28 FRIDAY

CARD OF THE DAY:

▷ INTENTION

▷ REFLECTION

APR 29 SATURDAY

CARD OF THE DAY:

▷ INTENTION

▷ REFLECTION

APR 30 SUNDAY

CARD OF THE DAY:

▷ INTENTION

▷ REFLECTION

INSIGHTS

MAY

THE HANGED MAN

After celebrating and gaining closure with the World in April, the Hanged Man now invites you to slow down and hit 'pause' on your regular routine. You are in between phases or cycles, and you might like to take a creative break so you can replenish your energy and let your creative juices flow in your own time and space. Surrender and see the world from a different perspective so you can embrace new opportunities that will only become apparent once you slow down.

THE HANGED MAN

🪷 RITUAL: RELEASE AND LET GO

- ◎ Find a place outside where you can lie on the ground and not be disturbed.

- ◎ Before you lie down, find the Hanged Man in your favorite deck and draw in the energy of this powerful card.

- ◎ Then, lie yourself down comfortably on the ground. Feel yourself relax into the ground, and as you slowly let go and surrender, feel the earth supporting you.

- ◎ Look up into the sky and notice how different it looks from this perspective. Notice the clouds passing by in different shapes, and the gradients of color reaching out into the Universe.

- ◎ Take three long, deep breaths, and notice how comfortably the earth holds you. As you breathe out, feel your body, mind, and soul release anything that no longer serves you into the wide, open sky.

- ◎ When you're ready, slowly rise and write your insights into your Planner.

🧘 CRYSTAL: AMAZONITE

The soothing green color of Amazonite has a grounding effect on your soul and spirit. Use this stone to help quiet your mind and allow new perspectives to come through.

INSIGHTS

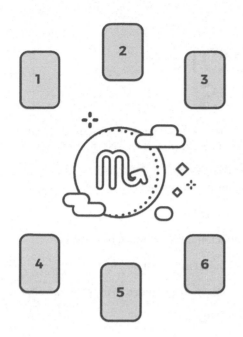

MAY 5 | LUNAR ECLIPSE

FULL MOON IN SCORPIO

Intense energies surround the Scorpio Full Moon, setting the stage for shadow work and transformational activities. Use this energy to release anything that no longer resonates with your true self.

1. What feelings have I been avoiding?

2. What lessons have I learned through trying times in the past six months?

3. What intense emotions are coming up for me now?

4. How can I express my emotions more healthily?

5. What do I need to release in order to experience deep transformation?

6. Where do I need to relinquish control in my life?

INSIGHTS

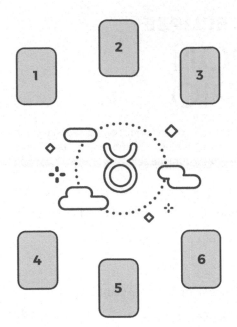

MAY 19

NEW MOON IN TAURUS

With the New Moon in Taurus, you have the chance to consciously create peaceful and pleasurable experiences in your life. Use this energy to develop empowering new habits.

1. What can I do to inspire tranquility in my home?

2. What lessons can I learn from nature?

3. How can I release unhealthy attachments to physical possessions?

4. What simple pleasures would I most enjoy right now?

5. What activities will help me become more grounded in my physical self?

6. What can I do to manage overindulgence?

INSIGHTS

Don't forget to snap a pic of your reading and share on IG using the hashtag #biddytarotplanner.
We love seeing you using your Biddy Tarot Planner in action and can't wait to celebrate with you!

MAY 01 SATURDAY   CARD OF THE DAY:

▷ INTENTION   ▷ REFLECTION

MAY 02 SUNDAY   CARD OF THE DAY:

▷ INTENTION   ▷ REFLECTION

MAY 03 MONDAY   CARD OF THE DAY:

▷ INTENTION   ▷ REFLECTION

MAY 04 TUESDAY   CARD OF THE DAY:

▷ INTENTION   ▷ REFLECTION

MAY 05 WEDNESDAY | ● *Full Moon in Scorpio*   CARD OF THE DAY:

▷ INTENTION   ▷ REFLECTION

MAY 06 THURSDAY   CARD OF THE DAY:

▷ INTENTION   ▷ REFLECTION

MAY 07 FRIDAY   CARD OF THE DAY:

▷ INTENTION   ▷ REFLECTION

MAY 08 SATURDAY

CARD OF THE DAY:

▷ INTENTION

▷ REFLECTION

MAY 09 SUNDAY

CARD OF THE DAY:

▷ INTENTION

▷ REFLECTION

MAY 10 MONDAY

CARD OF THE DAY:

▷ INTENTION

▷ REFLECTION

MAY 11 TUESDAY

CARD OF THE DAY:

▷ INTENTION

▷ REFLECTION

MAY 12 WEDNESDAY

CARD OF THE DAY:

▷ INTENTION

▷ REFLECTION

MAY 13 THURSDAY

CARD OF THE DAY:

▷ INTENTION

▷ REFLECTION

MAY 14 FRIDAY | *Mercury Retrograde ends*

CARD OF THE DAY:

▷ INTENTION

▷ REFLECTION

MAY 15   SATURDAY

CARD OF THE DAY:

▷ INTENTION

▷ REFLECTION

MAY 16   SUNDAY

CARD OF THE DAY:

▷ INTENTION

▷ REFLECTION

MAY 17   MONDAY

CARD OF THE DAY:

▷ INTENTION

▷ REFLECTION

MAY 18   TUESDAY

CARD OF THE DAY:

▷ INTENTION

▷ REFLECTION

MAY 19   WEDNESDAY | ○ *New Moon in Taurus*

CARD OF THE DAY:

▷ INTENTION

▷ REFLECTION

MAY 20   THURSDAY

CARD OF THE DAY:

▷ INTENTION

▷ REFLECTION

MAY 21   FRIDAY

CARD OF THE DAY:

▷ INTENTION

▷ REFLECTION

MAY 22   SATURDAY   CARD OF THE DAY:

▷ INTENTION   ▷ REFLECTION

MAY 23   SUNDAY   CARD OF THE DAY:

▷ INTENTION   ▷ REFLECTION

MAY 24   MONDAY   CARD OF THE DAY:

▷ INTENTION   ▷ REFLECTION

MAY 25   TUESDAY   CARD OF THE DAY:

▷ INTENTION   ▷ REFLECTION

MAY 26   WEDNESDAY   CARD OF THE DAY:

▷ INTENTION   ▷ REFLECTION

MAY 27   THURSDAY   CARD OF THE DAY:

▷ INTENTION   ▷ REFLECTION

MAY 28   FRIDAY   CARD OF THE DAY:

▷ INTENTION   ▷ REFLECTION

MAY 29 SATURDAY

CARD OF THE DAY:

▷ INTENTION

▷ REFLECTION

MAY 30 SUNDAY

CARD OF THE DAY:

▷ INTENTION

▷ REFLECTION

MAY 31 MONDAY

CARD OF THE DAY:

▷ INTENTION

▷ REFLECTION

INSIGHTS

JUNE

THE MAGICIAN

It's time to activate your manifestation superpowers, my friend! With the Magician, you have everything you need to make your dreams a reality this June. Connect with your vision, gather your tools and resources, and start putting your ideas into action. Now is the perfect time to move forward on an idea that you recently conceived. The seed of potential has sprouted, and you are being called to take action and bring your intention to fruition.

RITUAL: MANIFEST YOUR VISION

- ⊙ Pull out the Magician from your favorite Tarot deck and place the card nearby to serve as your guide throughout this ritual.

- ⊙ On a piece of paper, write down your vision for a new idea that has been on your mind. What is it that you want to bring into fruition?

- ⊙ Then, brainstorm all of the tools and resources that you already have available to you and how you can use them to bring your dream to life.

- ⊙ Finally, close your eyes and visualize your goal. See everything effortlessly falling into place to achieve your dream.

- ⊙ When you're ready, open your eyes and say out loud, "So be it!"

CRYSTAL: SMOKY QUARTZ

Smoky Quartz helps absorb negative energy and supports positive mental health. It's the perfect stone to protect against negative energy and aid in grounding and cord-cutting. Be sure to regularly cleanse and charge your Smoky Quartz with a favorite herb bundle, or by the light of the Full Moon.

INSIGHTS

JUNE 3

FULL MOON IN SAGITTARIUS

You can expect heightened ideas and visions during this Full Moon in Sagittarius. Tap into this expansive energy and release anything that's keeping you small.

1. Where do I need to focus on expanding my awareness?

2. What do I need to release in order to achieve my goals?

3. What is my ideal vision for the global community?

4. How might short- or long-term travel benefit me in the next six months?

5. What can I do to connect more deeply with my friends?

6. What do I need to let go of in order to truly inspire others?

INSIGHTS

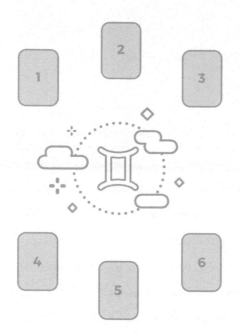

JUNE 17

NEW MOON IN GEMINI

A fresh New Moon in Gemini brings a sense of lightness. Set intentions around what you want to learn and teach, and how you can communicate for maximum effect.

1. How can I enhance my perceptions of the world around me?

2. What am I most curious about right now?

3. Where do I need to learn to verbalize my emotions?

4. What do I have to teach others?

5. What lessons can I learn from others?

6. How can I communicate with others in new and innovative ways?

INSIGHTS

JUN 01 THURSDAY   CARD OF THE DAY:

▷ INTENTION   ▷ REFLECTION

JUN 02 FRIDAY   CARD OF THE DAY:

▷ INTENTION   ▷ REFLECTION

JUN 03 SATURDAY | ● *Full Moon in Sagittarius*   CARD OF THE DAY:

▷ INTENTION   ▷ REFLECTION

JUN 04 SUNDAY   CARD OF THE DAY:

▷ INTENTION   ▷ REFLECTION

JUN 05 MONDAY   CARD OF THE DAY:

▷ INTENTION   ▷ REFLECTION

JUN 06 TUESDAY   CARD OF THE DAY:

▷ INTENTION   ▷ REFLECTION

JUN 07 WEDNESDAY   CARD OF THE DAY:

▷ INTENTION   ▷ REFLECTION

JUN 08 THURSDAY

CARD OF THE DAY:

▷ INTENTION

▷ REFLECTION

JUN 09 FRIDAY

CARD OF THE DAY:

▷ INTENTION

▷ REFLECTION

JUN 10 SATURDAY

CARD OF THE DAY:

▷ INTENTION

▷ REFLECTION

JUN 11 SUNDAY

CARD OF THE DAY:

▷ INTENTION

▷ REFLECTION

JUN 12 MONDAY

CARD OF THE DAY:

▷ INTENTION

▷ REFLECTION

JUN 13 TUESDAY

CARD OF THE DAY:

▷ INTENTION

▷ REFLECTION

JUN 14 WEDNESDAY

CARD OF THE DAY:

▷ INTENTION

▷ REFLECTION

JUN 15   THURSDAY

CARD OF THE DAY:

▷ INTENTION

▷ REFLECTION

JUN 16   FRIDAY

CARD OF THE DAY:

▷ INTENTION

▷ REFLECTION

JUN 17   SATURDAY | ○ New Moon in Gemini

CARD OF THE DAY:

▷ INTENTION

▷ REFLECTION

JUN 18   SUNDAY

CARD OF THE DAY:

▷ INTENTION

▷ REFLECTION

JUN 19   MONDAY

CARD OF THE DAY:

▷ INTENTION

▷ REFLECTION

JUN 20   TUESDAY

CARD OF THE DAY:

▷ INTENTION

▷ REFLECTION

JUN 21   WEDNESDAY

CARD OF THE DAY:

▷ INTENTION

▷ REFLECTION

JUN 22   THURSDAY   CARD OF THE DAY:

▷ INTENTION   ▷ REFLECTION

JUN 23   FRIDAY   CARD OF THE DAY:

▷ INTENTION   ▷ REFLECTION

JUN 24   SATURDAY   CARD OF THE DAY:

▷ INTENTION   ▷ REFLECTION

JUN 25   SUNDAY   CARD OF THE DAY:

▷ INTENTION   ▷ REFLECTION

JUN 26   MONDAY   CARD OF THE DAY:

▷ INTENTION   ▷ REFLECTION

JUN 27   TUESDAY   CARD OF THE DAY:

▷ INTENTION   ▷ REFLECTION

JUN 28   WEDNESDAY   CARD OF THE DAY:

▷ INTENTION   ▷ REFLECTION

JUN 29 THURSDAY CARD OF THE DAY:

▷ INTENTION ▷ REFLECTION

JUN 30 FRIDAY CARD OF THE DAY:

▷ INTENTION ▷ REFLECTION

INSIGHTS

SUMMER SOLSTICE SPREAD

The Summer Solstice (June 21, 7:57am PT / December 22, 1:27pm AEST) is the time to shine and be seen! Watch as your projects crest towards completion and you feel a burst of energy to take action on the new opportunities that arose during the Springtime.

Use the following Tarot spread around the time of the Summer Solstice to connect with this sacred energy.

1. What new opportunities have emerged over the Spring?

2. How can I bring my current projects to fruition?

3. What is expanding in my life right now?

4. What blessings am I receiving?

5. What truly fulfills me?

6. How can I shine my light in the world?

INSIGHTS

INSIGHTS

SUMMER SOLSTICE INTENTIONS

Holding the energy and insight of your Summer Solstice Tarot Reading, set your intentions for the next three months:

JULY

THE LOVERS

The Lovers card invites you to create conscious connections this month. Invest in relationships with people who light you up and raise your vibration. But also look to those people who may trigger or challenge you — these relationships are here to serve you and show you what you need to accept within yourself. Open your heart to give and receive love this month, and nurture your relationships with others through kindness and loving acceptance.

 ### RITUAL: OPENING THE HEART

- ⊙ To begin, take out the Lovers card from your Tarot deck and reflect on its energy.

- ⊙ Then, find a quiet place and light a candle and burn some rose or ylang-ylang oil.

- ⊙ Close your eyes and connect with your heart chakra and visualize a ball of pink light radiating from your heart center.

- ⊙ Feel this light growing and growing as it fills your body, then radiates out into your aura, your room, your neighborhood, and eventually into the world and the Universe beyond. Take a moment to feel this deep, radiant love.

- ⊙ Say this affirmation 3 times — "I honor the love inside me and connect consciously with others."

- ⊙ When you're ready, open your eyes and journal about your experience.

CRYSTAL: ROSE QUARTZ

Rose Quartz is the stone of peace and unconditional love. It's effective in drawing in loving relationships and deflecting negative energies. Rose Quartz will help you open your heart to love and beauty by healing unexpressed heartaches and transmuting internalized pains that no longer serve you.

INSIGHTS

JULY 3
FULL MOON IN CAPRICORN

The Full Moon in Capricorn is a powerful time to reflect on your achievements. Where have you stood in integrity and built something you're proud of?

1. What am I most proud of achieving in the past six months?

2. What foundations do I most need to establish now to support future success?

3. What is a non-negotiable for me right now?

4. How can I help motivate others to work toward their own goals?

5. Which limiting beliefs are preventing me from setting bigger goals?

6. Where do I need to make more ethical choices?

INSIGHTS

JULY 17

NEW MOON IN CANCER

The New Moon in Cancer is one of the best opportunities to make conscious choices about how you experience your everyday life. Dive into your emotional world and set empowering intentions around how you want to feel.

1. What new feelings are coming up for me right now?

2. Where do I need to empower myself to be more vulnerable in my relationships?

3. How might I benefit from setting boundaries?

4. How can I level-up my self-care practice?

5. What do I need to know about creating sacred space in my home?

6. What new approach can I take to support my emotional well-being?

INSIGHTS

JUL 01   SATURDAY   CARD OF THE DAY:

▷ INTENTION   ▷ REFLECTION

JUL 02   SUNDAY   CARD OF THE DAY:

▷ INTENTION   ▷ REFLECTION

JUL 03   MONDAY | ● *Full Moon in Capricorn*   CARD OF THE DAY:

▷ INTENTION   ▷ REFLECTION

JUL 04   TUESDAY   CARD OF THE DAY:

▷ INTENTION   ▷ REFLECTION

JUL 05   WEDNESDAY   CARD OF THE DAY:

▷ INTENTION   ▷ REFLECTION

JUL 06   THURSDAY   CARD OF THE DAY:

▷ INTENTION   ▷ REFLECTION

JUL 07   FRIDAY   CARD OF THE DAY:

▷ INTENTION   ▷ REFLECTION

JUL 08   SATURDAY   CARD OF THE DAY:

▷ INTENTION   ▷ REFLECTION

JUL 09   SUNDAY   CARD OF THE DAY:

▷ INTENTION   ▷ REFLECTION

JUL 10   MONDAY   CARD OF THE DAY:

▷ INTENTION   ▷ REFLECTION

JUL 11   TUESDAY   CARD OF THE DAY:

▷ INTENTION   ▷ REFLECTION

JUL 12   WEDNESDAY   CARD OF THE DAY:

▷ INTENTION   ▷ REFLECTION

JUL 13   THURSDAY   CARD OF THE DAY:

▷ INTENTION   ▷ REFLECTION

JUL 14   FRIDAY   CARD OF THE DAY:

▷ INTENTION   ▷ REFLECTION

JUL 15   SATURDAY   CARD OF THE DAY:

▷ INTENTION   ▷ REFLECTION

JUL 16   SUNDAY   CARD OF THE DAY:

▷ INTENTION   ▷ REFLECTION

JUL 17   MONDAY | ○ *New Moon in Cancer*   CARD OF THE DAY:

▷ INTENTION   ▷ REFLECTION

JUL 18   TUESDAY   CARD OF THE DAY:

▷ INTENTION   ▷ REFLECTION

JUL 19   WEDNESDAY   CARD OF THE DAY:

▷ INTENTION   ▷ REFLECTION

JUL 20   THURSDAY   CARD OF THE DAY:

▷ INTENTION   ▷ REFLECTION

JUL 21   FRIDAY   CARD OF THE DAY:

▷ INTENTION   ▷ REFLECTION

JUL 22   SATURDAY   CARD OF THE DAY:

▷ INTENTION   ▷ REFLECTION

JUL 23   SUNDAY   CARD OF THE DAY:

▷ INTENTION   ▷ REFLECTION

JUL 24   MONDAY   CARD OF THE DAY:

▷ INTENTION   ▷ REFLECTION

JUL 25   TUESDAY   CARD OF THE DAY:

▷ INTENTION   ▷ REFLECTION

JUL 26   WEDNESDAY   CARD OF THE DAY:

▷ INTENTION   ▷ REFLECTION

JUL 27   THURSDAY   CARD OF THE DAY:

▷ INTENTION   ▷ REFLECTION

JUL 28   FRIDAY   CARD OF THE DAY:

▷ INTENTION   ▷ REFLECTION

JUL 29 SATURDAY CARD OF THE DAY:

▷ INTENTION ▷ REFLECTION

JUL 30 SUNDAY CARD OF THE DAY:

▷ INTENTION ▷ REFLECTION

JUL 31 MONDAY CARD OF THE DAY:

▷ INTENTION ▷ REFLECTION

INSIGHTS

AUGUST

THE EMPRESS

The Empress welcomes you into August with abundant, creative, and fertile energy. The time is ripe to bring your next big project to fruition. Ask yourself, "What am I creating and nurturing? What can I birth into the world?" Your creativity is closely aligned to the beauty you see around you. So, take a moment to find beauty in all things, no matter how small or ordinary, and use it to inspire your creative projects.

THE EMPRESS

✿ RITUAL: SELF-NURTURE

One of the best ways to nurture your ideas to fruition is to nurture yourself first. When your cup is full, you have the energy and the space to create and birth your ideas.

- ⊙ Find the Empress card in your deck and set up a small altar around your card with items that represent beauty, such as flowers, crystals, and fruit.

- ⊙ Take a moment to close your eyes, and visualize yourself surrounded by everything you need to bring your ideas into fruition. Feel this abundant energy in every cell of your body.

- ⊙ Then, open your eyes and write down all the ways you can nurture yourself throughout this month so that you are fully supported in your creative pursuits. Ask the Empress to guide you and draw upon her energy.

- ⊙ Close out the ritual by placing these ideas on your altar so you can view them each day and remind yourself of your commitment to your self-care and nurturing.

⚗ CRYSTAL: MOONSTONE

Nurture yourself with the hopeful, soothing and inspirational energy of Moonstone. Moonstone supports you in unlocking the power of your inner goddess. Just like the Moon, even if you can't see it, the energy of the Moonstone is there, pulling on your inner tides and setting your own natural rhythms back in balance.

INSIGHTS

AUGUST 1
FULL MOON IN AQUARIUS

This Full Moon in Aquarius amplifies the energy of the water bearer, bringing it into laser-sharp focus. Consider the impact your day-to-day choices may be having on a much wider, even global, scale.

1. How can I utilize my unique gifts to contribute to global change?

2. Which beliefs may be having a detrimental affect on my community?

3. What global causes can I champion to have a greater impact on the world?

4. How can I help others to examine their beliefs about the global community?

5. Which forms of communication might I need to limit or release?

6. What can I do to empower others to become more vulnerable?

INSIGHTS

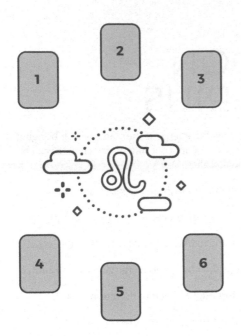

AUGUST 16

NEW MOON
IN LEO

Your creations and passions are coming into focus with the new moon in Leo. Now is the time to set courageous intentions about how you want to show up in the world.

1. What do I most want to create?

2. What can I do to express myself authentically in healthy, empowered ways?

3. What new aspects of myself am I discovering?

4. How can I be an effective and compassionate leader?

5. Where am I best placed to lead by example?

6. Which areas of my life may require a little more courage in the next six months?

INSIGHTS

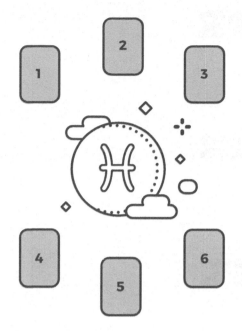

AUGUST 30
FULL MOON
IN PISCES

A dreamy Full Moon in Pisces can intensify your connection to spirit and your intuition. Celebrate the manifestation of your imaginings and release any wishful thinking that isn't serving you now.

1. Which areas of my life have benefited most from my intuition?

2. What do I need to release in order to connect with myself on a deeper level?

3. Where do I need to focus more gratitude in the next six months?

4. What limiting beliefs must I release to expand my creative projects?

5. What can I focus on to deepen my spiritual practice?

6. How might the arts inspire my own creative success moving forward?

INSIGHTS

AUG 01   TUESDAY | ● *Full Moon in Aquarius*   CARD OF THE DAY:

▷ INTENTION   ▷ REFLECTION

AUG 02   WEDNESDAY   CARD OF THE DAY:

▷ INTENTION   ▷ REFLECTION

AUG 03   THURSDAY   CARD OF THE DAY:

▷ INTENTION   ▷ REFLECTION

AUG 04   FRIDAY   CARD OF THE DAY:

▷ INTENTION   ▷ REFLECTION

AUG 05   SATURDAY   CARD OF THE DAY:

▷ INTENTION   ▷ REFLECTION

AUG 06   SUNDAY   CARD OF THE DAY:

▷ INTENTION   ▷ REFLECTION

AUG 07   MONDAY   CARD OF THE DAY:

▷ INTENTION   ▷ REFLECTION

AUG 08 TUESDAY   CARD OF THE DAY:

▷ INTENTION   ▷ REFLECTION

AUG 09 WEDNESDAY   CARD OF THE DAY:

▷ INTENTION   ▷ REFLECTION

AUG 10 THURSDAY   CARD OF THE DAY:

▷ INTENTION   ▷ REFLECTION

AUG 11 FRIDAY   CARD OF THE DAY:

▷ INTENTION   ▷ REFLECTION

AUG 12 SATURDAY   CARD OF THE DAY:

▷ INTENTION   ▷ REFLECTION

AUG 13 SUNDAY   CARD OF THE DAY:

▷ INTENTION   ▷ REFLECTION

AUG 14 MONDAY   CARD OF THE DAY:

▷ INTENTION   ▷ REFLECTION

AUG 15 TUESDAY

CARD OF THE DAY:

▷ INTENTION

▷ REFLECTION

AUG 16 WEDNESDAY | ☼ *New Moon in Leo*

CARD OF THE DAY:

▷ INTENTION

▷ REFLECTION

AUG 17 THURSDAY

CARD OF THE DAY:

▷ INTENTION

▷ REFLECTION

AUG 18 FRIDAY

CARD OF THE DAY:

▷ INTENTION

▷ REFLECTION

AUG 19 SATURDAY

CARD OF THE DAY:

▷ INTENTION

▷ REFLECTION

AUG 20 SUNDAY

CARD OF THE DAY:

▷ INTENTION

▷ REFLECTION

AUG 21 MONDAY

CARD OF THE DAY:

▷ INTENTION

▷ REFLECTION

AUG 22   TUESDAY   CARD OF THE DAY:

▷ INTENTION   ▷ REFLECTION

AUG 23   WEDNESDAY | *Mercury Retrograde begins* CARD OF THE DAY:

▷ INTENTION   ▷ REFLECTION

AUG 24   THURSDAY   CARD OF THE DAY:

▷ INTENTION   ▷ REFLECTION

AUG 25   FRIDAY   CARD OF THE DAY:

▷ INTENTION   ▷ REFLECTION

AUG 26   SATURDAY   CARD OF THE DAY:

▷ INTENTION   ▷ REFLECTION

AUG 27   SUNDAY   CARD OF THE DAY:

▷ INTENTION   ▷ REFLECTION

AUG 28   MONDAY   CARD OF THE DAY:

▷ INTENTION   ▷ REFLECTION

AUG 29   TUESDAY

CARD OF THE DAY:

▷ INTENTION

▷ REFLECTION

AUG 30   WEDNESDAY | ● *Full Moon in Pisces*

CARD OF THE DAY:

▷ INTENTION

▷ REFLECTION

AUG 31   THURSDAY

CARD OF THE DAY:

▷ INTENTION

▷ REFLECTION

INSIGHTS

SEPTEMBER

XIII

DEATH

DEATH

September brings change and transformation, death and rebirth. What must (metaphorically) die within you so that a newer, more evolved version of yourself can emerge? As you continue to evolve, you're also rapidly outgrowing yourself — and this is a good thing! The time has come to shed your skin, let go of the past, and create new ways of being that are more in alignment with who you truly want to become. Though it may be difficult, the Death card promises renewal and transformation. Remember, if you resist necessary endings, you may experience pain — both emotionally and physically. But if you can visualize new possibilities, you allow more constructive patterns to emerge.

✿ RITUAL: DEATH AND REBIRTH

This is a powerful ritual, but also very intense — so please enter into it mindfully.

- ⊙ Take out the Death card and light a candle. Meditate on what the concept of death and transformation means to you.

- ⊙ When you're ready, bring your attention inwards and connect with your inner source of energy.

- ⊙ Imagine that today is the last day of your life. You are stripped of your past and your identity, and all that's left is your pure source energy. You may even imagine yourself melting into the ground and fading away.

- ⊙ Then, imagine yourself being reborn and recreated from that pure source of energy. Experience a sense of peace and deep truth as you step fully into this transformation. You are refreshed and revitalized.

- ⊙ When you're ready, come back into the room and journal about your experience.

⚜ CRYSTAL: CARNELIAN

Known to help instill acceptance of "the cycle of life," Carnelian grounds you in present reality. This powerful stone helps you trust yourself and your perceptions so you can recognize what no longer serves you. Carnelian also stimulates courage and helps you overcome long-term negative conditioning.

INSIGHTS

SEPTEMBER 14
NEW MOON IN VIRGO

The new moon in Virgo is an opportunity to get clear on how you want to be of service in the world. What intentions can you set around mastering skills or concepts? What will the best version of yourself focus on during this lunar cycle?

1. How can I be of highest service to my family, friends and partner?

2. Which area of my life would benefit most from a fresh routine?

3. What change might I make to support my physical health and well-being?

4. What action can I take to bring a sense of order to my home environment?

5. What action can I take to process my thoughts more effectively?

6. What action can I take to gain further emotional clarity?

INSIGHTS

FULL MOON IN ARIES

Honor your inner warrior with the Full Moon in Aries. Celebrate the ways you've grown into your strength, and release the fears that hold you back.

1. Where would I benefit most from being more fearless?

2. How can I release stress in a more constructive way?

3. Which battle is it time to release attachment to?

4. Where do I most need to be a little more selfish?

5. What do I need to release to be able to feel strong?

6. How can I be more compassionate toward others?

INSIGHTS

SEP 01   FRIDAY   CARD OF THE DAY:

▷ INTENTION   ▷ REFLECTION

SEP 02   SATURDAY   CARD OF THE DAY:

▷ INTENTION   ▷ REFLECTION

SEP 03   SUNDAY   CARD OF THE DAY:

▷ INTENTION   ▷ REFLECTION

SEP 04   MONDAY   CARD OF THE DAY:

▷ INTENTION   ▷ REFLECTION

SEP 05   TUESDAY   CARD OF THE DAY:

▷ INTENTION   ▷ REFLECTION

SEP 06   WEDNESDAY   CARD OF THE DAY:

▷ INTENTION   ▷ REFLECTION

SEP 07   THURSDAY   CARD OF THE DAY:

▷ INTENTION   ▷ REFLECTION

SEP 08 FRIDAY

CARD OF THE DAY:

▷ INTENTION

▷ REFLECTION

SEP 09 SATURDAY

CARD OF THE DAY:

▷ INTENTION

▷ REFLECTION

SEP 10 SUNDAY

CARD OF THE DAY:

▷ INTENTION

▷ REFLECTION

SEP 11 MONDAY

CARD OF THE DAY:

▷ INTENTION

▷ REFLECTION

SEP 12 TUESDAY

CARD OF THE DAY:

▷ INTENTION

▷ REFLECTION

SEP 13 WEDNESDAY

CARD OF THE DAY:

▷ INTENTION

▷ REFLECTION

SEP 14 THURSDAY | ○ *New Moon in Virgo*

CARD OF THE DAY:

▷ INTENTION

▷ REFLECTION

SEP 15 FRIDAY | *Mercury Retrograde ends*   CARD OF THE DAY:

▷ INTENTION   ▷ REFLECTION

SEP 16 SATURDAY   CARD OF THE DAY:

▷ INTENTION   ▷ REFLECTION

SEP 17 SUNDAY   CARD OF THE DAY:

▷ INTENTION   ▷ REFLECTION

SEP 18 MONDAY   CARD OF THE DAY:

▷ INTENTION   ▷ REFLECTION

SEP 19 TUESDAY   CARD OF THE DAY:

▷ INTENTION   ▷ REFLECTION

SEP 20 WEDNESDAY   CARD OF THE DAY:

▷ INTENTION   ▷ REFLECTION

SEP 21 THURSDAY   CARD OF THE DAY:

▷ INTENTION   ▷ REFLECTION

SEP 22 FRIDAY   CARD OF THE DAY:

▷ INTENTION   ▷ REFLECTION

SEP 23 SATURDAY   CARD OF THE DAY:

▷ INTENTION   ▷ REFLECTION

SEP 24 SUNDAY   CARD OF THE DAY:

▷ INTENTION   ▷ REFLECTION

SEP 25 MONDAY   CARD OF THE DAY:

▷ INTENTION   ▷ REFLECTION

SEP 26 TUESDAY   CARD OF THE DAY:

▷ INTENTION   ▷ REFLECTION

SEP 27 WEDNESDAY   CARD OF THE DAY:

▷ INTENTION   ▷ REFLECTION

SEP 28 THURSDAY   CARD OF THE DAY:

▷ INTENTION   ▷ REFLECTION

SEP 29   FRIDAY | ● *Full Moon in Aries*   CARD OF THE DAY:

▷ INTENTION

▷ REFLECTION

SEP 30   SATURDAY   CARD OF THE DAY:

▷ INTENTION

▷ REFLECTION

INSIGHTS

FALL EQUINOX SPREAD

The Fall Equinox (September 22, 11:49pm PT / March 21, 7:24am AEST) is the time of harvest. After the abundance of the Summer, it's time to reap what you've sown, celebrate with deep appreciation, then bunker down for the Winter season. This is the perfect time for slowing down, expressing gratitude for what you've achieved, and gathering your resources for the Winter period.

Use the following Tarot spread around the Fall Equinox to connect with this sacred energy.

1. What have I achieved during the Summer period?

2. What is the bounty of my harvest?

3. What am I truly grateful for?

4. What resources are available to me now?

5. What resources do I need to gather?

6. What can I release and let go?

INSIGHTS

INSIGHTS

FALL EQUINOX INTENTIONS

Holding the energy and insight of your Fall Equinox Tarot Reading, set your intentions for the next three months:

OCTOBER

THE EMPEROR

The presence of the Emperor calls on you to implement the structure and discipline you need to create long-lasting success in October. In order to receive the abundance you deserve, you must first create a solid foundation and structure designed to fully support it. Enough play — it's now time to work! Get serious about what you want to manifest in your life and stay focused on your goals. If you spend time this month creating disciplined structure and strategic systems in your life, you'll see significant progress.

IV

THE EMPEROR

✿ RITUAL: YOUR IDEAL DAILY SCHEDULE

⊙ As you start this ritual, ask yourself, "What does a dream day look like for me?" How would you start your day? What would you do throughout the day? How would you feel by the end of the day? Write down your answers in your journal.

⊙ Next, create a daily schedule, based on your dream day. Be intentional about where you choose to invest your time and energy.

⊙ To close out the ritual, find the Emperor card in your favorite deck, and tune into his structured energy. What message of support and advice does he have for you as you embark on your ideal daily schedule?

⚗ CRYSTAL: TIGER'S EYE

Tiger's Eye is a masculine stone known to strengthen will, mental clarity, and the good judgment needed to maintain focus. Work with it this month to help you balance your emotions and manifest your boldest goals.

INSIGHTS

OCTOBER 14 | SOLAR ECLIPSE
NEW MOON
IN LIBRA

The New Moon in Libra is a beautiful time to explore your personal values and the environment and relationships that support you in feeling balanced.

1. Where in my life would I benefit most from a deeper sense of harmony?

2. How might evaluating my personal style have a positive impact on my life?

3. How can I create more beauty in my environment?

4. Where would I benefit from a more peaceful approach?

5. How can I bond more strongly with others?

6. What is my true intention in my current or future relationship?

INSIGHTS

OCTOBER 28 | LUNAR ECLIPSE

FULL MOON IN TAURUS

The Taurus Full Moon Lunar Eclipse brings the focus to your physical resources and sense of peace. Luxuriate in sensual pleasures and release anything that feels like drama.

1. Which resources that I have gathered in the past six months will bring me the most joy?

2. What can I do to inspire more serenity in my life?

3. What do I need to do to feel more physically grounded?

4. How can I achieve a sense of absolute presence in my relationships?

5. What can I let go of now to make life feel easy?

6. How might my current or future relationship benefit from better understanding my sensuality?

INSIGHTS

OCT 01   SUNDAY

CARD OF THE DAY:

▷ INTENTION

▷ REFLECTION

OCT 02   MONDAY

CARD OF THE DAY:

▷ INTENTION

▷ REFLECTION

OCT 03   TUESDAY

CARD OF THE DAY:

▷ INTENTION

▷ REFLECTION

OCT 04   WEDNESDAY

CARD OF THE DAY:

▷ INTENTION

▷ REFLECTION

OCT 05   THURSDAY

CARD OF THE DAY:

▷ INTENTION

▷ REFLECTION

OCT 06   FRIDAY

CARD OF THE DAY:

▷ INTENTION

▷ REFLECTION

OCT 07   SATURDAY

CARD OF THE DAY:

▷ INTENTION

▷ REFLECTION

OCT 08 SUNDAY   CARD OF THE DAY:

▷ INTENTION   ▷ REFLECTION

OCT 09 MONDAY   CARD OF THE DAY:

▷ INTENTION   ▷ REFLECTION

OCT 10 TUESDAY   CARD OF THE DAY:

▷ INTENTION   ▷ REFLECTION

OCT 11 WEDNESDAY   CARD OF THE DAY:

▷ INTENTION   ▷ REFLECTION

OCT 12 THURSDAY   CARD OF THE DAY:

▷ INTENTION   ▷ REFLECTION

OCT 13 FRIDAY   CARD OF THE DAY:

▷ INTENTION   ▷ REFLECTION

OCT 14 SATURDAY | ○ *New Moon in Libra*   CARD OF THE DAY:

▷ INTENTION   ▷ REFLECTION

OCT 15 SUNDAY

CARD OF THE DAY:

▷ INTENTION

▷ REFLECTION

OCT 16 MONDAY

CARD OF THE DAY:

▷ INTENTION

▷ REFLECTION

OCT 17 TUESDAY

CARD OF THE DAY:

▷ INTENTION

▷ REFLECTION

OCT 18 WEDNESDAY

CARD OF THE DAY:

▷ INTENTION

▷ REFLECTION

OCT 19 THURSDAY

CARD OF THE DAY:

▷ INTENTION

▷ REFLECTION

OCT 20 FRIDAY

CARD OF THE DAY:

▷ INTENTION

▷ REFLECTION

OCT 21 SATURDAY

CARD OF THE DAY:

▷ INTENTION

▷ REFLECTION

OCT 22   SUNDAY   CARD OF THE DAY:

▷ INTENTION   ▷ REFLECTION

OCT 23   MONDAY   CARD OF THE DAY:

▷ INTENTION   ▷ REFLECTION

OCT 24   TUESDAY   CARD OF THE DAY:

▷ INTENTION   ▷ REFLECTION

OCT 25   WEDNESDAY   CARD OF THE DAY:

▷ INTENTION   ▷ REFLECTION

OCT 26   THURSDAY   CARD OF THE DAY:

▷ INTENTION   ▷ REFLECTION

OCT 27   FRIDAY   CARD OF THE DAY:

▷ INTENTION   ▷ REFLECTION

OCT 28   SATURDAY | ● *Full Moon in Taurus*   CARD OF THE DAY:

▷ INTENTION   ▷ REFLECTION

OCT 29 SUNDAY

CARD OF THE DAY:

▷ INTENTION

▷ REFLECTION

OCT 30 MONDAY

CARD OF THE DAY:

▷ INTENTION

▷ REFLECTION

OCT 31 TUESDAY

CARD OF THE DAY:

▷ INTENTION

▷ REFLECTION

INSIGHTS

NOVEMBER

VIII

STRENGTH

STRENGTH

The Strength card represents inner strength, determination, and power. This month, feel the fear and do it anyway! If you've been going through a rough time and feel burnt out and stressed, the Strength card gives you the courage to find the power within yourself to persevere. You've got what it takes to see this situation through to its eventual end. And if you find yourself with extra strength and energy, you may be willing to step up and hold space for someone who needs your strength and support.

🪷 RITUAL: I AM STRONG

⊙ Find the Strength card in your deck and gaze at this card as you take in its energy and power.

⊙ Light a candle and focus on the flame as you reconnect with the fiery spirit within yourself.

⊙ On a piece of paper, write down, "I am strong because..." and continue writing for at least 5-10 minutes or until you feel complete.

⊙ Then, read each statement out aloud, feeling your inner strength rising with every word.

⊙ Lock in that feeling of courage by taking a moment to close your eyes and visualize yourself as strong and fearless, able to overcome any challenge.

⊙ To close the ritual, blow out the candle and place your strength affirmations where you'll be able to see them each day.

🔥 CRYSTAL: BLOODSTONE

Known as "the warrior stone," Bloodstone helps infuse you with resilience and courage to handle any obstacle in your path. Carry a piece with you in challenging times to help give you the inner strength you need to persevere.

INSIGHTS

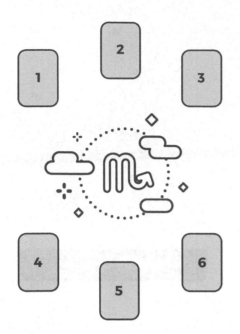

NOVEMBER 13
NEW MOON IN SCORPIO

The New Moon in Scorpio is the ideal time to make conscious decisions about your spiritual transformation. Use this time to set your intentions about who you're becoming and where you'd like to go.

1. Which area of my life might experience the deepest transformation in the next six months?

2. How can I healthily express my deepest desires?

3. Which elements of my shadow self need some attention and care?

4. How can I release the desire to control or manipulate outcomes?

5. Where am I not being truly honest with myself?

6. How can I foster a deeper connection with my spiritual truth?

INSIGHTS

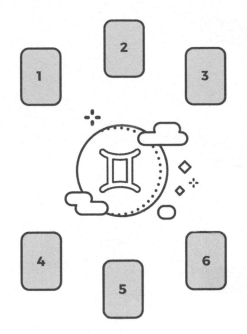

FULL MOON IN GEMINI

The Full Moon in Gemini enhances your vitality and brings to light the ways you perceive the world. Release any feelings of boredom and explore your curiosities.

1. How have my perceptions of the world around me changed in the last 6 months?

2. What new information have I learned that I can teach others?

3. How has verbalizing my emotions impacted my closest relationships this year?

4. What valuable lessons have I learned from others?

5. What valuable lessons have I been able to teach others?

6. How can I approach problems in a more logical and calculated way?

INSIGHTS

NOV 01 WEDNESDAY
CARD OF THE DAY:

▷ INTENTION

▷ REFLECTION

NOV 02 THURSDAY
CARD OF THE DAY:

▷ INTENTION

▷ REFLECTION

NOV 03 FRIDAY
CARD OF THE DAY:

▷ INTENTION

▷ REFLECTION

NOV 04 SATURDAY
CARD OF THE DAY:

▷ INTENTION

▷ REFLECTION

NOV 05 SUNDAY
CARD OF THE DAY:

▷ INTENTION

▷ REFLECTION

NOV 06 MONDAY
CARD OF THE DAY:

▷ INTENTION

▷ REFLECTION

NOV 07 TUESDAY
CARD OF THE DAY:

▷ INTENTION

▷ REFLECTION

NOV 08 WEDNESDAY

CARD OF THE DAY:

▷ INTENTION

▷ REFLECTION

NOV 09 THURSDAY

CARD OF THE DAY:

▷ INTENTION

▷ REFLECTION

NOV 10 FRIDAY

CARD OF THE DAY:

▷ INTENTION

▷ REFLECTION

NOV 11 SATURDAY

CARD OF THE DAY:

▷ INTENTION

▷ REFLECTION

NOV 12 SUNDAY

CARD OF THE DAY:

▷ INTENTION

▷ REFLECTION

NOV 13 MONDAY | ○ *New Moon in Scorpio*

CARD OF THE DAY:

▷ INTENTION

▷ REFLECTION

NOV 14 TUESDAY

CARD OF THE DAY:

▷ INTENTION

▷ REFLECTION

NOV 15 WEDNESDAY | CARD OF THE DAY:

▷ INTENTION | ▷ REFLECTION

NOV 16 THURSDAY | CARD OF THE DAY:

▷ INTENTION | ▷ REFLECTION

NOV 17 FRIDAY | CARD OF THE DAY:

▷ INTENTION | ▷ REFLECTION

NOV 18 SATURDAY | CARD OF THE DAY:

▷ INTENTION | ▷ REFLECTION

NOV 19 SUNDAY | CARD OF THE DAY:

▷ INTENTION | ▷ REFLECTION

NOV 20 MONDAY | CARD OF THE DAY:

▷ INTENTION | ▷ REFLECTION

NOV 21 TUESDAY | CARD OF THE DAY:

▷ INTENTION | ▷ REFLECTION

NOV 22 WEDNESDAY   CARD OF THE DAY:

▷ INTENTION   ▷ REFLECTION

NOV 23 THURSDAY   CARD OF THE DAY:

▷ INTENTION   ▷ REFLECTION

NOV 24 FRIDAY   CARD OF THE DAY:

▷ INTENTION   ▷ REFLECTION

NOV 25 SATURDAY   CARD OF THE DAY:

▷ INTENTION   ▷ REFLECTION

NOV 26 SUNDAY   CARD OF THE DAY:

▷ INTENTION   ▷ REFLECTION

NOV 27 MONDAY | ● *Full Moon in Gemini*   CARD OF THE DAY:

▷ INTENTION   ▷ REFLECTION

NOV 28 TUESDAY   CARD OF THE DAY:

▷ INTENTION   ▷ REFLECTION

NOV 29　WEDNESDAY

CARD OF THE DAY:

▷ INTENTION

▷ REFLECTION

NOV 30　THURSDAY

CARD OF THE DAY:

▷ INTENTION

▷ REFLECTION

INSIGHTS

DECEMBER

0

THE FOOL

THE FOOL

What a beautiful way to end the year! You started 2023 with the Chariot and a desire to take bold action to achieve your goals. And now, with the Fool card in December, you're releasing the need to always be in control. You're receptive to the new beginnings and opportunities that are coming to you, without pretense or expectation. You're open to living life to the fullest and seeing the world through completely new eyes. This month, take joy in the gifts that the world has to offer you right now. This is also the perfect time to take a leap of faith and step into the unknown, knowing that it could bring you amazing opportunities beyond what you've ever imagined. Be fun and spontaneous. Forget your routine and schedule this month — be free!

RITUAL: NEVER HAVE I EVER

- Write a list of things you've never tried before. Activities you've never attempted, food you haven't tried, towns or suburbs you've never visited, unique travel destinations, or tackling new crafts. If it comes to your mind, write it down!

- Each week, pick three things from your list and do them! For example, in our family we have Magical Mystery Tours. We randomly pick a nearby suburb, and then we spend the whole day there, trying out new cafes, parks, walks, and museums. You won't always find these on TripAdvisor, but it makes for a fun day of exploration!

CRYSTAL: DALMATIAN STONE

The Dalmatian Stone helps you to tune into your inner-child and stimulate a sense of playfulness and fun. This stone will help you get out of your head and into your body to fully experience the world around you.

INSIGHTS

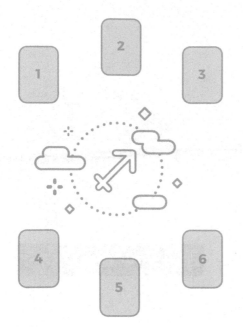

DECEMBER 12

NEW MOON
IN SAGITTARIUS

The New Moon in Sagittarius encourages you to expand your awareness and perspective. Set intentions around adventures and experiences that will broaden your worldview.

1. Where do I need to focus on expanding my awareness?

2. What can I do to inspire a sense of adventure in my life?

3. What can I do to expand my friendship circles and connect with new people?

4. What is my ideal vision for the global community?

5. What lessons have I learned from short or long-term travel in the past 6 months?

6. How can I utilize those lessons to inspire others?

INSIGHTS

DECEMBER 26
FULL MOON
IN CANCER

The Full Moon in Cancer is the best time to release any feelings that you're holding onto. Dive into your emotional world and set empowering intentions around what feelings you want to release.

1. What new feelings are coming up for me right now that need to be released?

2. Where do I need to empower myself to be more vulnerable in my relationships?

3. How might I benefit from setting boundaries?

4. How can I level-up my self-care practice?

5. What do I need to know about creating sacred space in my home?

6. What new approach can I take to support my emotional well-being?

INSIGHTS

DEC 01   FRIDAY   CARD OF THE DAY:

▷ INTENTION   ▷ REFLECTION

DEC 02   SATURDAY   CARD OF THE DAY:

▷ INTENTION   ▷ REFLECTION

DEC 03   SUNDAY   CARD OF THE DAY:

▷ INTENTION   ▷ REFLECTION

DEC 04   MONDAY   CARD OF THE DAY:

▷ INTENTION   ▷ REFLECTION

DEC 05   TUESDAY   CARD OF THE DAY:

▷ INTENTION   ▷ REFLECTION

DEC 06   WEDNESDAY   CARD OF THE DAY:

▷ INTENTION   ▷ REFLECTION

DEC 07   THURSDAY   CARD OF THE DAY:

▷ INTENTION   ▷ REFLECTION

DEC 08 FRIDAY

CARD OF THE DAY:

▷ INTENTION

▷ REFLECTION

DEC 09 SATURDAY

CARD OF THE DAY:

▷ INTENTION

▷ REFLECTION

DEC 10 SUNDAY

CARD OF THE DAY:

▷ INTENTION

▷ REFLECTION

DEC 11 MONDAY

CARD OF THE DAY:

▷ INTENTION

▷ REFLECTION

DEC 12 TUESDAY | ○ New Moon in Sagittarius
Mercury Retrograde begins

CARD OF THE DAY:

▷ INTENTION

▷ REFLECTION

DEC 13 WEDNESDAY

CARD OF THE DAY:

▷ INTENTION

▷ REFLECTION

DEC 14 THURSDAY

CARD OF THE DAY:

▷ INTENTION

▷ REFLECTION

DEC 15 FRIDAY

CARD OF THE DAY:

▷ INTENTION

▷ REFLECTION

DEC 16 SATURDAY

CARD OF THE DAY:

▷ INTENTION

▷ REFLECTION

DEC 17 SUNDAY

CARD OF THE DAY:

▷ INTENTION

▷ REFLECTION

DEC 18 MONDAY

CARD OF THE DAY:

▷ INTENTION

▷ REFLECTION

DEC 19 TUESDAY

CARD OF THE DAY:

▷ INTENTION

▷ REFLECTION

DEC 20 WEDNESDAY

CARD OF THE DAY:

▷ INTENTION

▷ REFLECTION

DEC 21 THURSDAY

CARD OF THE DAY:

▷ INTENTION

▷ REFLECTION

DEC 22 FRIDAY

CARD OF THE DAY:

▷ INTENTION

▷ REFLECTION

DEC 23 SATURDAY

CARD OF THE DAY:

▷ INTENTION

▷ REFLECTION

DEC 24 SUNDAY

CARD OF THE DAY:

▷ INTENTION

▷ REFLECTION

DEC 25 MONDAY

CARD OF THE DAY:

▷ INTENTION

▷ REFLECTION

DEC 26 TUESDAY | ● *Full Moon in Cancer*

CARD OF THE DAY:

▷ INTENTION

▷ REFLECTION

DEC 27 WEDNESDAY

CARD OF THE DAY:

▷ INTENTION

▷ REFLECTION

DEC 28 THURSDAY

CARD OF THE DAY:

▷ INTENTION

▷ REFLECTION

DEC 29 FRIDAY
CARD OF THE DAY:

▷ INTENTION

▷ REFLECTION

DEC 30 SATURDAY
CARD OF THE DAY:

▷ INTENTION

▷ REFLECTION

DEC 31 SUNDAY
CARD OF THE DAY:

▷ INTENTION

▷ REFLECTION

INSIGHTS

WINTER SOLSTICE SPREAD

The Winter Solstice (December 21 7:27pm PT/June 22, 12:57am AEST), is the perfect time to go within and hibernate. It's time to reflect on your shadow self — the part of you that you try to deny or hide from others. Through this self-reflection, you'll emerge once again into the light as your most powerful self.

Use the following Tarot spread during the Winter Solstice to connect with this sacred energy.

1. What is the essence of my inner shadow self?

2. What can I learn from my shadow self?

3. How can I bring my shadow self into the light?

4. What lights me up from within?

5. What new seeds am I planting?

6. What do I need to release in order to create space for growth?

INSIGHTS

INSIGHTS

WINTER SOLSTICE INTENTIONS

Holding the energy and insight of your Winter Solstice Tarot Reading, set your intentions for the next three months:

2023 REFLECTION

As we come to the end of 2023, take some time to reflect on the past 12 months and prepare yourself for the year to come. Go back to the New Year's Tarot Spread you completed in January and reflect on what has emerged over the course of the year.

Then, go through the questions below and for each one, journal your intuitive thoughts first, then if you feel called to do so, draw a Tarot card to help you go deeper.

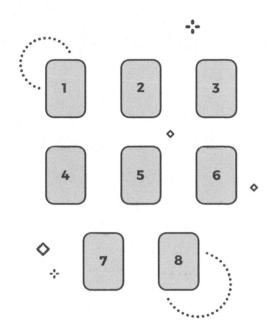

1. What were my biggest achievements for 2023?

2. What were my biggest challenges for 2023?

3. How have I developed as a person?

4. What did I learn in 2023?

5. How would I describe 2023 in just three words?

6. What is now complete?

7. What continues into 2024?

8. What new seeds and opportunities are being planted?

1. WHAT WERE MY BIGGEST ACHIEVEMENTS FOR 2023?

2. WHAT WERE MY BIGGEST CHALLENGES FOR 2023?

3. HOW HAVE I DEVELOPED AS A PERSON?

4. WHAT DID I LEARN IN 2023?

5. HOW WOULD I DESCRIBE 2023 IN JUST THREE WORDS?

6. WHAT IS NOW COMPLETE?

7. WHAT CONTINUES INTO 2024?

8. WHAT NEW SEEDS AND OPPORTUNITIES ARE BEING PLANTED?

LEARN TO READ TAROT INTUITIVELY...

Access these Biddy Tarot learning resources to activate your intuition and reach YOUR highest potential. Learn more about these resources — and our full range of Tarot courses and programs — to help you on your journey at www.biddytarot.com/shop.

THE ULTIMATE GUIDE TO TAROT CARD MEANINGS
Fresh, Modern, Practical Guide To The Meanings Of Every Tarot Card

The *Ultimate Guide to Tarot Card Meanings* has everything you need to read the Tarot cards as simply as reading a magazine. Just imagine — all the Tarot card meanings you could ever want, right at your fingertips in this comprehensive, 400+ page reference guide. You'll never need to buy another book on Tarot card meanings again!

Available for purchase at www.biddytarot.com/guide.

INTUITIVE TAROT: 31 DAYS TO LEARN TO READ TAROT CARDS AND DEVELOP YOUR INTUITION
Trust Your Intuition, Access Your Inner Power, And Bring The Divine Into Your Everyday Life

With *Intuitive Tarot*, you can learn to access your intuition and confidently read the cards without a reference guide. Imagine the thrill of looking at a card (or even a full Tarot spread) and instantly understanding the message it has for you. Through 31 daily lessons and activities, you'll learn to quickly and accurately interpret the cards, and unlock the secrets to an insightful reading. It's already inside you — you just need to trust it.

Available for purchase at www.biddytarot.com/tarot-guides/intuitive-tarot.

TAROT 101
A Step-By-Step Beginner Video Series and Workbook for Tarot Lovers Everywhere

Do you want to learn to connect with the Tarot and trust your intuition? *Tarot 101* is the ultimate course for Tarot beginners eager to harness the powerful messages of the cards. The guided program features in-depth lessons, including steps on how to do readings with clarity and tell an accurate and insightful story with the cards. Are you ready to start your Tarot journey? Sign up for the *Tarot 101* program today!

Available for purchase at www.biddytarot.com/tarot-101-course.

MASTER THE TAROT
CARD MEANINGS

MASTER THE TAROT CARD MEANINGS PROGRAM

Stop Memorizing the Cards and Start Listening to Your Intuition

The *Master the Tarot Card Meanings* program will help you learn to read Tarot from your heart, not a book. Each lesson empowers you to build a unique personal connection with the Tarot, using simple yet powerful techniques for interpreting the cards. In just seven modules, you'll unlock the secrets of the Major and Minor Arcana, Court Cards, and reversed readings using Numerology, Symbolism, and so much more. By the end of the program, you'll have the power to intuitively access the meaning behind any spread!

Available for purchase at www.biddytarot.com/mtcm.

THE BIDDY TAROT COMMUNITY

Join a global, online community of 2000+ Tarot lovers and develop your Tarot reading skills

The Biddy Tarot Community is the only online community of its kind. Connect with 2,000+ Tarot lovers all over the world and get resources to help you learn and grow in your practice. Members get access to an expansive library of Tarot resources, the practice reading platform, and a unique TarotPath to help you level up on your Tarot journey.

Join the Biddy Tarot Community at www.biddytarot.com/community.

Made in the USA
Columbia, SC
29 December 2022